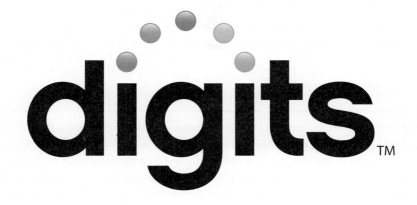

Program Overview Guide

PEARSON

Boston, Massachusetts • Chandler, Arizona • Glenview, Illinois • Upper Saddle River, New Jersey

Acknowledgments

viii Pearson Education. Photo by Andrew Wallace; **9** ifong/Shutterstock; **13** Pearson Education. Photo by Andrew Wallace; **38** Killroy/iStockphoto; **74** ifong/Shutterstock; **77** Pearson Education. Photo by Andrew Wallace; **106** Monkey Business Images/Shutterstock

ISBN-13: 978-0-13-320825-2
ISBN-10: 0-13-320825-7
6 7 8 9 10 11 12 V064 16 15 14 13 12

digits™ System Requirements

Supported System Configurations

	Operating System (32-bit only)	Web Browser* (32-bit only)	Java™ (JRE) Version**	JavaScript® Version***
PC	Windows® XP (SP3)	Internet Explorer® 7	Version 5.0, Update 11 or higher	1.4.2
	Windows Vista (SP1)	Internet Explorer 8	Version 5.0, Update 11 or higher	1.5
	Windows 7	Internet Explorer 9 (in compatibility mode)	Version 6.0, up to Update 18	1.6
Mac	Macintosh® OS 10.6	Safari® 5.0 and 5.1	Version 5.0, Update 16 or higher	1.5

   * Pop-up blockers must be disabled in the browser.
  ** Java (JRE) plug-in must be installed.
 *** JavaScript must be enabled in the browser.

Additional Requirements

Software	Version
Adobe® Flash®	Version 10.1 or higher
Adobe Reader® (required for PC*)	Version 8 or higher
Word processing software	Microsoft® Word®, Open Office, or similar application to open ".doc" files

* Macintosh® OS 10.6 has a built-in PDF reader, Preview.

Screen Resolution
Minimum: 1024 x 768*
Maximum: 1280 x 1024
*recommended for interactive whiteboards

Internet Connection
Broadband (cable/DSL) or greater is recommended.

Firefox® and Chrome™ Users
You cannot use the Firefox or Chrome browsers to log in or view courses.

AOL® and AT&T™ Yahoo!® Users
You cannot use the AOL or AT&T Yahoo! browsers. However, you can use AOL or AT&T as your Internet Service Provider to access the Internet, and then open a supported browser.

Francis (Skip) Fennell
***digits* Author**

Approaches to mathematics content and curriculum, educational policy, and support for intervention

Dr. Francis (Skip) Fennell is Professor of Education at McDaniel College, and a senior author with Pearson. He is a past president of the National Council of Teachers of Mathematics (NCTM) and a member of the writing team for the Curriculum Focal Points from the NCTM, which influenced the work of the Common Core Standards Initiative. Skip was also one of the writers of the Principles and Standards for School Mathematics.

Art Johnson
***digits* Author**

Approaches to mathematical content and support for English Language Learners

Art Johnson is a Professor of Mathematics at Boston University who taught in public school for over 30 years. He is part of the author team for Pearson's high school mathematics series. Art is the author of numerous books, including Teaching Mathematics to Culturally and Linguistically Diverse Students published by Allyn & Bacon, Teaching Today's Mathematics in the Middle Grades published by Allyn & Bacon, and Guiding Children's Learning of Mathematics, K–6 published by Wadsworth.

Helene Sherman
***digits* Author**

Teacher education and support for struggling students

Helene Sherman is Associate Dean for Undergraduate Education and Professor of Education in the College of Education at the University of Missouri in St. Louis, MO. Helene is the author of Teaching Learners Who Struggle with Mathematics, published by Merrill.

Stuart J. Murphy
***digits* Author**

Visual learning and student engagement

Stuart J. Murphy is a visual learning specialist and the author of the MathStart series. He contributed to the development of the Visual Learning Bridge in enVisionMATH™ as well as many visual elements of the Prentice Hall Algebra 1, Geometry, and Algebra 2 high school program.

Janie Schielack
***digits* Author**

Approaches to mathematical content, building problem solvers,and support for intervention

Janie Schielack is Professor of Mathematics and Associate Dean for Assessment and PreK–12 Education at Texas A&M University. She chaired the writing committee for the NCTM Curriculum Focal Points and was part of the nine-member NCTM feedback and advisory team that responded to and met with CCSSCO and NGA representatives during the development of various drafts of the Common Core State Standards.

Eric Milou
***digits* Author**

Approaches to mathematical content and the use of technology in middle grades classrooms

Eric Milou is Professor in the Department of Mathematics at Rowan University in Glassboro, NJ. Eric teaches pre-service teachers and works with in-service teachers, and is primarily interested in balancing concept development with skill proficiency. He was part of the nine-member NCTM feedback/advisory team that responded to and met with Council of Chief State School Officers (CCSSCO) and National Governors Association (NGA) representatives during the development of various drafts of the Common Core State Standards. Eric is the author of Teaching Mathematics to Middle School Students, published by Allyn & Bacon.

William F. Tate
digits Author
Approaches to intervention, and use of efficacy and research

William Tate is the Edward Mallinckrodt Distinguished University Professor in Arts & Sciences at Washington University in St. Louis, MO. He is a past president of the American Educational Research Association. His research focuses on the social and psychological determinants of mathematics achievement and attainment as well as the political economy of schooling.

Randall I. Charles
digits Advisor

Dr. Randall I. Charles is Professor Emeritus in the Department of Mathematics at San Jose State University in San Jose, CA, and a senior author with Pearson. Randall served on the writing team for the Curriculum Focal Points from NCTM. The NCTM Curriculum Focal Points served as a key inspiration to the writers of the Common Core Standards in bringing focus, depth, and coherence to the curriculum.

> *Pearson tapped leaders in mathematics education to develop digits. This esteemed author team—from diverse areas of expertise including mathematical content, Understanding by Design, and Technology Engagement—came together to construct a highly interactive and personalized learning experience.*

Jim Cummins
digits Advisor
Supporting English Language Learners

Dr. Jim Cummins is Professor and Canada Research Chair in the Centre for Educational Research on Languages and Literacies at the University of Toronto. His research focuses on literacy development in multilingual school contexts as well as on the potential roles of technology in promoting language and literacy development.

Grant Wiggins
digits Consulting Author
Understanding by Design

Grant Wiggins is a cross-curricular Pearson consulting author specializing in curricular change. He is the author of Understanding by Design published by ASCD, and the President of Authentic Education in Hopewell, NJ. Over the past 20 years, he has worked on some of the most influential reform initiatives in the country, including Vermont's portfolio system and Ted Sizer's Coalition of Essential Schools.

Jacquie Moen
digits Advisor
Digital Technology

Jacquie Moen is a consultant specializing in how consumers interact with and use digital technologies. Jacquie worked for AOL for 10 years, and most recently was VP & General Manager for AOL's kids and teen online services, reaching over seven million kids every month. Jacquie has worked with a wide range of organizations to develop interactive content and strategies to reach families and children, including National Geographic, PBS, Pearson Education, National Wildlife Foundation, and the National Children's Museum.

Contents

Teaching

Supporting English Language Learners

Appendix

> "If we teach **today** as we taught **yesterday**, we rob our children of **tomorrow**.
>
> –John Dewey

Overview

The Role of Classroom Technology

Today is both an exciting and chaotic time. As never before, teachers can choose from many new classroom technologies to engage and motivate students.

Pearson's new comprehensive and coherent middle grades math program *digits* offers integrated instructional content designed both to optimize teachers' and students' time and to personalize learning. Created with the teacher in mind, the program simplifies typically laborious tasks and enables teachers to focus on teaching and interacting with students.

The *digits* program helps teachers leverage the classroom technology that they have, whether that includes a projector, an interactive whiteboard, student response systems, or devices that support one-to-one computing. More important, the program can grow with classrooms as technology is introduced. To use *digits*, a classroom needs only a computer and a projector.

Research and Policy

The development of *digits* has been driven by the Common Core State Standards for Mathematics (CCSSM), Understanding by Design, and foundational research in instruction, data-driven intervention, and motivation. Each driver has provided fundamental, unique, and interlinking contributions to the program.

The CCSSM have identified the instructional goals and the achievement expectations of students at each grade level. They do not necessarily outline how to achieve those goals, but rather establish a common framework to prepare students and gauge success. Prior to the initiative, state standards varied widely and curriculum conversations often did not cross state lines, as if each state had its own "language" when talking about and making decisions about math instruction. With the CCSSM, states are beginning to use one language and gain an ability to achieve long-term goals across many states.

Understanding by Design principles, on the other hand, have provided guidance on how to structure units and lessons in *digits* to achieve the content and practice goals of the Common Core State Standards. With a research-based approach for curriculum planning, Understanding by Design focuses on achieving the desired learning outcomes with coherence, and provides specific guidance on how to "unpack" the various layers in a standard.

While the Common Core State Standards identifies what students need to know and develop and Understanding by Design provides guidance on how to structure the lessons to achieve the instructional goals, foundational research in instruction, data-driven intervention, and motivation provides the inspiration for the actual learning activities. The convergence of these three factors has resulted in the ground breaking and unique approach in *digits* that is not only instructionally effective but also fun to teach!

Ⓒ Common Core State Standards

The Common Core State Standards provide a consistent, clear understanding of what students are expected to learn, so teachers and parents know what they need to do to help them. The standards are designed to be robust and relevant to the real world, reflecting the knowledge and skills that our young people need for success in college and careers. With American students fully prepared for the future, our communities will be best positioned to compete successfully in the global economy.

The Common Core State Standards were developed through a state-led effort coordinated by the National Governors Association Center for Best Practices and the Council of Chief State School Officers. The standards were informed and influenced by state standards, teachers, school administrators, content experts, international models, and the general public.

Generally, the CCSSM define the knowledge and skills students should have in order to be successful in college and in workforce training programs. For middle grades, the standards prepare students well for an Algebra 1 course in Grade 9. Further, students who have completed Grade 7 and mastered the content, skills, and understandings of the CCSSM through Grade 7 are prepared for an algebra course in Grade 8.

The standards stress not only procedural skill but also conceptual understanding. Combined, these emphases ensure that students are prepared for higher level mathematics in high school.

Each grade has a specific set of focused and coherent standards organized in clusters and domains.

Focus Areas of the Grade 6 CCSSM

- connecting ratio and rate to whole number multiplication and division and using concepts of ratio and rate to solve problems

- completing understanding of division of fraction and extending the notion of number to the system of rational numbers, including negative numbers

- writing, interpreting, and using expressions and equations

- developing understanding of statistical thinking

Focus Areas of the Grade 7 CCSSM

- developing understanding of and applying proportional relationships

- developing understanding of operations with rational numbers and working with expressions and linear equations

- solving problems involving scale drawings and informal geometric constructions, and working with two- and three-dimensional shapes to solve problems involving area, surface area, and volume

- drawing inferences about populations based on samples

Focus Areas of the Grade 8 CCSSM

- formulating and reasoning about expressions and equations, including modeling an association in bivariate data with a linear equation, and solving linear equations and systems of linear equations

- grasping the concept of a function and using functions to describe quantitative relationships

- analyzing two- and three-dimensional space and figures using distance, angle, similarity, and congruence, and understanding and applying the Pythagorean Theorem

In addition to Standards for Mathematical Content, the Common Core State Standards include Standards for Mathematical Practice, which describe habits that enable the development of deep mathematical understanding and expertise.

The Common Core Standards for Mathematical Practice focus on the processes and proficiencies that all mathematics educators should seek to develop in their students. The eight standards were informed by the National Council of Teachers of Mathematics Process Standards (2000) and the strands of mathematical proficiency outlined in Adding It Up by the National Research Council (2001).

References for Common Core State Standards

"Common Core State Standards Initiative | About The Standards." Common Core State Standards Initiative | Home. Web 06 Apr. 2011. http://www.corestandards.org/.

National Council of Teachers of Mathematics, (2000). Principles and Standards for School Mathematics. Reston, VA: NCTM.

National Research Council. (2001). Adding It Up: Helping Children Learn Mathematics (J. Kilpatrick, J. Swafford, & B. Findell, Eds.) Washington, DC: National Academy Press.

Understanding by Design Principles

Understanding by Design is a curriculum-planning framework that focuses on helping students understand important ideas in a meaningful way. The research-based approach of Understanding by Design aims to have students demonstrate understanding through sense making and transfer of learning through authentic performance.

Understanding by Design involves a three-stage "backward-design" process that uses the desired learning outcomes and the evidence that learning has occurred as the main drivers. During Stage 1, the desired results are identified, which include the targeted goals, the essential questions that students should consider, and the knowledge and skills that the students will need. In Stage 2, developers and curriculum planners determine the acceptable evidence such as what performances and products students will need to demonstrate or create, as well as the acceptable assessment criteria. Lastly, in Stage 3, the learning experiences and instruction are planned accordingly.

References for Understanding by Design

Wiggins, G., & McTighe, J. (1998). Understanding by Design. Alexandria, VA: Association for Supervision and Curriculum Development.

Wiggins, G., & McTighe, J. (2011) The Understanding by Design Guide to Creating High-Quality Units. Alexandria, VA: Association for Supervision and Curriculum Development.

Foundational Research

The inspiration of *digits* was driven by three foundational pillars of research: *Instruction*, *Data-Driven Intervention*, and *Motivation*. Key elements of each of these pillars are described below.

Instruction

Research based on students who struggle with math indicates that **successful programs include a balance of explicit instruction and guided explorations**. Explicit instruction is most effective for presentation of factual content; guided explorations are most effective for content that is conceptual, procedural, or problem-based.

Positive results have been found by preparing students prior to a formal learning structure. This preparation involves introducing them to concepts through active learning.

A **differentiated classroom** provides multiple avenues for acquiring information and processing and making sense of ideas enabling each student to learn effectively.

Whole-class instruction is most feasible for middle grades teachers and allows for direct instruction of content followed by engaging discussions and sharing a variety of methods.

Small-group work enables students to provide mutual feedback and engage in debates that motivate students to abandon misconceptions and search for better solutions.

Peer-assisted learning allows students to quickly compare and correct understandings by working with classmates who may have insight into areas of struggle.

Research clearly emphasizes that for learning to occur, new information must be integrated with what the learner already knows. By **activating prior knowledge** before an assessment, students can draw on what they already know for a more accurate assessment picture.

Online tools provide significant functionality in transmitting information to the student, providing forums for exchange, increased opportunities for learning, and alternative formats for information gathering. This type of environment permits the instructor to build one course while implementing a variety of resources to best meet student needs.

Data-Driven Intervention

Diagnostic tests yield strengths and weaknesses about students' mathematics learning and provide information for teachers to plan appropriate instruction and to group students.

Research indicates that **formative assessment followed by feedback** during learning activities is the most effective instructional strategy. In fact, consistent and ongoing formative assessment has been found to increase learning effectiveness by as much as seventy-five percent.

Research recommends that a **strong technology infrastructure** can make formative assessment feasible by enabling students to take assessments online and providing immediate feedback to both the student and the teacher.

Motivation

Findings from the National Math Panel report together with Pearson-sponsored research suggest that one of teachers' greatest challenges in helping students succeed in mathematics is **working with unmotivated students**.

The **transition for children from elementary school to middle school** is most often a challenging one, and this has a negative impact on motivation in academic classes.

Developmental changes in students' intrinsic motivation are generally accompanied by declining confidence and by increasing anxiety.

Intrinsic motivation can be increased by challenging students, giving them some control, letting them use technology, and helping them meet success.

Cognitive neuroscience research indicates that **positive mood triggered by humor** enhances insight and the ability to solve problems.

Differentiated assignments enable students to draw on their own readiness levels and learning modes, thereby drawing on students' interests and strengths. Students can grow from appropriate challenges while the teacher retains focus on the key content that is essential to all learners.

Students who work with a visual organizer are better able to follow the flow of a lecture. This type of tool can help students focus on key ideas and information.

Educational research shows that if information is conveyed to the students in a combination of text, color, graphics, animation, sound, moving pictures, and a degree of interactivity, the **interactive multimedia approach may result in a significant increase in retention and improvement in the learning rate**.

References for Foundational Research

Black, P., and Wiliam, D. (1998). Assessment and classroom learning. Assessment in Education: Principles, Policy and Practice 5(1), 7-74.

Dwyer, D., Barbieri, K., & Doerr, H. Creating a Virtual Classroom for Interactive Education on the Web. The Third International World Wide Web Conference. 1995.

Ehly, S. & Topping, K. (Eds.). (1998). Peer-Assisted Learning. Mahwah, NJ: Lawrence Erlbaum Associates.

Gurganus, S.P. (2007). Math Instruction for Students with Learning Problems. Boston, MA: Pearson Allyn & Bacon.

Kennelly, L. & Monrad, M. (2007). Approaches to Dropout Prevention: Heeding Early Warning Signs with Appropriate Interventions. Washington, DC: National High School Center at the American Institutes for Research.

Kramarski, B. & Mevarech, Z. R. (2003). Enhancing Mathematical Reasoning in the Classroom: The Effects of Cooperative Learning and Megacognitive Training. American Educational Research Journal, 40(1), 291-310.

Meece, J.L., Pintrich, P.R., & Schunk, D.H. (2008). Motivation in Education: Theory, Research, and Application. Upper Saddle River, NJ: Pearson Merrill Prentice Hall.

National Mathematics Advisory Panel. (2008). Foundations for Success: The Final Report of the National Mathematics Advisory Panel. Washington, DC: U.S. Department of Education.

Rumelhart, D. E. (1980). "Schemata: The building blocks of cognition." In R. J. Spiro et al., (Eds.) Theoretical Issues in Reading Comprehension (pp. 33-58). Hillsdale, NJ: Erlbaum.

State Educational Technology Directors Association. (2008). Technology Based Assessments Improve Teaching and Learning. Glen Burnie: MD.

Subramaniam, K., Kounios, J., Parrish, T., & Jung-Beeman, M. (2008). A Brain Mechanism for Facilitation of Insight by Positive Effect. Journal of Cognitive Neuroscience 21(3), 415-432.

Sullivan, Amy. (2008) Designing the Digital Classroom. Research Matters. Utah State University Research.

Tomlinson, C. (2001). How to Differentiate Instruction in Mixed-Ability Classrooms. Alexandria, VA: ASCD.

U.S. Department of Education, Institute of Education Sciences, National Center for Education Statistics.

Vahey, P., Yarnall, L., Patton, C., Zalles, D., & Swan, K. (2006). Proceedings from American Educational Research Association: Mathematizing middle school: Results from a cross-disciplinary study of data literacy. San Francisco, CA.

Wang, G. Work in Progress – Preview, Exercise, Teaching and Learning in Digital Electronics Education. IEEE Frontiers in Education Conference. Purdue University, 2008.

Wiliam, D. (2007). Content then process: teacher learning communities in the service of formative assessment. In D. B. Reeves (Ed.), Ahead of the curve: the power of assessment to transform teaching and learning (pp. 183-204). Bloomington, IN: Solution Tree.

Wiliam, D. (2007b). Keeping learning on track: Formative assessment and the regulation of learning. In F.K. Lester, Jr. (Ed.), Second handbook of mathematics teaching and learning (pp. 1053-1098). Greenwich, CT: Information Age Publishing.

Wiliam. D., & Leahy, S. (2007). A theoretical foundation for formative assessment. In J. H. McMillan (Ed.), Formative classroom assessment: Research, theory and practice. New York, NY: Teachers College Press.

Wiliam, D., & Thompson, M. (2007). Integrating assessment with instruction: What will it take to make it work? In C.A. Dwyer (Ed.), The future of assessment: Shaping teaching and learning. Mahwah, NJ: Lawrence Erlbaum Associates.

Developing *digits*

Taking *digits* from conception to reality has been an exciting process that involved teachers and students nationwide. Advances in technology enabled us to have greater transparency, engage with more educators than ever before, field test prototypes with hundreds of students, and respond agilely to student and teacher feedback.

Gathering Input

In addition to observing middle grades teachers nationwide to internalize their daily challenges and victories, we also invited teachers to Pearson IdeaShare, where they could express specific desires to be incorporated in a new middle grades math program. Teachers who joined Pearson IdeaShare could contribute ideas, read ideas from others, and vote on ideas in the categories of best practices and real world mathematical contexts. All ideas were carefully considered and over 90% of the ideas were incorporated into *digits*.

Iterative Field Testing

Early in the development process, we field tested Grade 6 and Grade 7 lessons with approximately 600 students in order to gain insight on implementation challenges, lesson flow, and degree of teacher fidelity. Adjustments were made following each field test cycle to respond to gathered feedback and observations. The following materials were included in the field tests:

- Readiness Assessment administered to students prior to instruction. A teacher report with recommended student differentiation groups for the Readiness Lesson was generated from the results of the assessment.

- Instruction on Ratios and Patterns and Functions, including the Readiness Lesson and on-level lessons (delivered online with back-up CD-ROM).

- Printed copies of teacher notes for each day's lesson.

- Student booklet containing the accompanying student companion pages.

- Student Dashboard and homework powered by Math XL for School.

Highlights from the iterative field tests that informed our thinking include:

- Overall program approach and key components were well received.

- In-class presentation was effective for presenting the instruction and keeping students engaged.

- Online homework with immediate feedback was motivating for students and time-saving for teachers.

- Online homework with supportive learning aids improved homework completion rates.

- Built-in differentiation informed by an objective assessment allowed teachers to spend more time with struggling students while providing on-level and advanced students authentic math experiences.

- Strong teacher materials helped support fidelity of implementation.

Evaluation

To increase teacher contribution, national teleconferences were conducted. In advance of the teleconferences, participants reviewed a self-guided presentation of the instructional model, the daily lesson routine, differentiation options, program components, and online homework. Participants were also able to interact with digital samples of the interactive whiteboard lessons as well as samples of pages from the student companion. Highlights from the teleconferences that informed our thinking include:

- Teachers believe mathematics education needs to integrate technology to keep up with the way students learn.

- Teachers praised the increased focus on differentiation and personalization found in **digits**.

- Teachers have heard promises of differentiation and time savings from other programs, but they believe this program would actually deliver on the promise.

- Teachers are concerned about technology reliability in schools and access at home. They found the available implementation options of *digits* helpful.

- Teachers want an ability to customize the materials to match their teaching style or to match class pacing needs. They found that *digits* provides this ability.

Ongoing evaluation includes a third party, multiple year, longitudinal efficacy study at sites nationwide beginning September 2011.

digits. delivers

- ☑ Integrated technology

- ☑ Differentiation and personalization

- ☑ Flexible technology implementation options for school and home

- ☑ Readily customizable materials

Mathematics Content

Building to the Common Core State Standards

Building to the Common Core State Standards requires a synthesis of both the Standards for Mathematical Content and the Standards for Mathematical Practice. While the content standards identify the core knowledge and skills that students are expected to possess at each grade level, the Standards for Mathematical Practice identify the attributes of mathematical thinking that teachers of all grades need to reinforce.

Consequently, building to the Common Core State Standards is more than just an alignment to the content standards. The *digits* program has been built to incorporate the Standards for Mathematical Practice in the overall instructional design. Multiple opportunities are provided daily to engage students in the use of the Standards for Mathematical Practice.

Common Core Standards for Mathematical Practice

digits incorporates the Standards for Mathematical Practice into the overall instructional design and pedagogical approach. *digits* focuses on providing teachers and students opportunities to develop mathematical proficiency by modeling and honing their Mathematical Practice as they work through the various problems and examples in the program.

The following highlights the opportunities these materials create to make Mathematical Practice a reality for students. It explains how *digits* supports the development of mathematical proficiency in students, citing some examples of how each Standard for Mathematical Practice is embedded in the *digits* curriculum.

Common Core State Standards for Mathematical Practice

1 Make sense of problems and persevere in solving them.

Mathematically proficient students start by explaining to themselves the meaning of a problem and looking for entry points to its solution. They analyze givens, constraints, relationships, and goals. They make conjectures about the form and meaning of the solution and plan a solution pathway rather than simply jumping into a solution attempt. They consider analogous problems, and try special cases and simpler forms of the original problem in order to gain insight into its solution. They monitor and evaluate their progress and change course if necessary. Older students might, depending on the context of the problem, transform algebraic expressions or change the viewing window on their graphing calculator to get the information they need. Mathematically proficient students can explain correspondences between equations, verbal descriptions, tables, and graphs or draw diagrams of important features and relationships, graph data, and search for regularity or trends. Younger students might rely on using concrete objects or pictures to help conceptualize and solve a problem. Mathematically proficient students check their answers to problems using a different method, and they continually ask themselves, "Does this make sense?" They can understand the approaches of others to solving complex problems and identify correspondences between different approaches.

Every lesson in *digits* engages students with the mathematical concept through problems designed to enable multiple entry points. Students approach the problems at their level of understanding and construct meaning through a balance of exploration, explicit instruction, and class collaboration. Through dynamic instructional tools, students evaluate various solution pathways to promote sense-making and critical thinking. As students learn, they are provided with feedback that helps them understand why the mathematics is important, as well as feedback that confirms thinking or redirects when appropriate. This feedback fosters independence and perseverance.

Additionally, learning aids in the online practice provide support only when students want and need it so that students can develop into confident and independent problem-solvers. *digits* promotes class collaboration and discourse through an inviting instructional design that supports a variety of mathematical strategies on the interactive whiteboard. Flexible digital tools enable the teacher to model Mathematical Practice and draw comparisons across student solution methods. Guidance in the teacher support materials includes probing questions to help students think through the process and construct meaning.

2 Reason abstractly and quantitatively.

Mathematically proficient students make sense of quantities and their relationships in problem situations. They bring two complementary abilities to bear on problems involving quantitative relationships: the ability to decontextualize—to abstract a given situation and represent it symbolically and manipulate the representing symbols as if they have a life of their own, without necessarily attending to their referents—and the ability to contextualize, to pause as needed during the manipulation process in order to probe into the referents for the symbols involved. Quantitative reasoning entails habits of creating a coherent representation of the problem at hand; considering the units involved; attending to the meaning of quantities, not just how to compute them; and knowing and flexibly using different properties of operations and objects.

Problems in *digits* are presented in a blend of both concrete and abstract representations to support abilities to decontextualize and contextualize. As students work with a concrete representation, they discover efficiencies by abstracting the given situation into symbolic representation that supports pursuit of a solution strategy. Conversely, abstract problems are also presented in *digits* that require dissection into order to understand the problem situation. Through thoughtful use of technology, problems in *digits* include visual and auditory cues such as movement and color-coding to assist students in the transfer between concrete and abstract. Real world objects morph into abstract shapes, which can consolidate into numeric or symbolic representation and vice versa. The dynamic visual and auditory presentation tangibly helps students develop their own mathematical thought processes.

3 Construct viable arguments and critique the reasoning of others.

Mathematically proficient students understand and use stated assumptions, definitions, and previously established results in constructing arguments. They make conjectures and build a logical progression of statements to explore the truth of their conjectures. They are able to analyze situations by breaking them into cases, and can recognize and use counterexamples. They justify their conclusions, communicate them to others, and respond to the arguments of others. They reason inductively about data, making plausible arguments that take into account the context from which the data arose. Mathematically proficient students are also able to compare the effectiveness of two plausible arguments, distinguish correct logic or reasoning from that which is flawed, and—if there is a flaw in an argument—explain what it is. Elementary students can construct arguments using concrete referents such as objects, drawings, diagrams, and actions. Such arguments can make sense and be correct, even though they are not generalized or made formal until later grades. Later, students learn to determine domains to which an argument applies. Students at all grades can listen or read the arguments of others, decide whether they make sense, and ask useful questions to clarify or improve the arguments.

digits supports class discourse with interactive whiteboard lessons. Students present solution strategies, defend them, and draw comparisons to other strategies by utilizing interactive presentation tools. Students are expected to articulate their thought processes and reasoning as well as critique the solutions of their peers. Practice problems include error analysis questions where students are asked to determine the reasonableness of sample student work and identify if and where an error was made.

The teacher support materials offers probing questions that support the development of a classroom culture that focuses on argument and critique as part of solving mathematical problems

4 Model with mathematics.

Mathematically proficient students can apply the mathematics they know to solve problems arising in everyday life, society, and the workplace. In early grades, this might be as simple as writing an addition equation to describe a situation. In middle grades, a student might apply proportional reasoning to plan a school event or analyze a problem in the community. By high school, a student might use geometry to solve a design problem or use a function to describe how one quantity of interest depends on another. Mathematically proficient students who can apply what they know are comfortable making assumptions and approximations to simplify a complicated situation, realizing that these may need revision later. They are able to identify important quantities in a practical situation and map their relationships using such tools as diagrams, two-way tables, graphs, flowcharts, and formulas. They can analyze those relationships mathematically to draw conclusions. They routinely interpret their mathematical results in the context of the situation and reflect on whether the results make sense, possibly improving the model if it has not served its purpose.

Because *digits* uses real world mathematical contexts, students recognize the inherent nature of mathematics as a means for modeling our world. Mathematics is purposefully used to deepen our understanding of the problem situation and provide opportunities to predict or solve for alternate scenarios or changes to conditions. Students routinely evaluate their mathematical results against the context of the situation to promote sense making. The interactive nature of *digits* allows students to experiment themselves with mathematical models in different forms. Thus students see the interrelationships among multiple representations.

5 Use appropriate tools strategically.

Mathematically proficient students consider the available tools when solving a mathematical problem. These tools might include pencil and paper, concrete models, a ruler, a protractor, a calculator, a spreadsheet, a computer algebra system, a statistical package, or dynamic geometry software. Proficient students are sufficiently familiar with tools appropriate for their grade or course to make sound decisions about when each of these tools might be helpful, recognizing both the insight to be gained and their limitations. For example, mathematically proficient high school students analyze graphs of functions and solutions generated using a graphing calculator. They detect possible errors by strategically using estimation and other mathematical knowledge. When making mathematical models, they know that technology can enable them to visualize the results of varying assumptions, explore consequences, and compare predictions with data. Mathematically proficient students at various grade levels are able to identify relevant external mathematical resources, such as digital content located on a website, and use them to pose or solve problems. They are able to use technological tools to explore and deepen their understanding of concepts.

In *digits,* students work with a wide array of math tools when solving problems. From simple pencil and paper in the student companion to digital tools on the interactive whiteboard or computer, students are constantly manipulating tools to support their construction of mathematical knowledge. Students must make decisions about which tools are most appropriate for a given problem situation and apply them. Because *digits* supports display of multiple tools, students can compare solution pathways and validate solutions using different tools and strategies. Through this ability to compare the effectiveness and efficiency of different tools for each problem situation, students are able to critically determine the most strategic application.

6 Attend to precision.

Mathematically proficient students try to communicate precisely to others. They try to use clear definitions in discussion with others and in their own reasoning. They state the meaning of the symbols they choose, including using the equal sign consistently and appropriately. They are careful about specifying units of measure, and labeling axes to clarify the correspondence with quantities in a problem. They calculate accurately and efficiently, express numerical answers with a degree of precision appropriate for the problem context. In the elementary grades, students give carefully formulated explanations to each other. By the time they reach high school they have learned to examine claims and make explicit use of definitions.

Since presentation and defense of solution strategies is foundational to the instructional design of *digits,* students are expected to communicate precisely and with clarity. To support communication and comprehension, key vocabulary and concepts can be accessed at any time with precise definitions, explanations, and supporting visuals. Vocabulary in context is also hyperlinked to its definitions so that students and teachers have immediate access at point of use. Additionally, lessons include a Key Concept review to reinforce and summarize the instructional intent of the lesson. As students communicate to others, these reference resources scaffold the development of precision and clarity.

7 Look for and make use of structure.

Mathematically proficient students look closely to discern a pattern or structure. Young students, for example, might notice that three and seven more is the same amount as seven and three more, or they may sort a collection of shapes according to how many sides the shapes have. Later, students will see 7×8 equals the well remembered $7 \times 5 + 7 \times 3$, in preparation for learning about the distributive property. In the expression $x^2 + 9x + 14$, older students can see the 14 as 2×7 and the 9 as $2 + 7$. They recognize the significance of an existing line in a geometric figure and can use the strategy of drawing an auxiliary line for solving problems. They also can step back for an overview and shift perspective. They can see complicated things, such as some algebraic expressions, as single objects or as being composed of several objects. For example, they can see $5 - 3(x - y)^2$ as 5 minus a positive number times a square and use that to realize that its value cannot be more than 5 for any real numbers x and y.

Through a balanced approach of exploration, explicit instruction, and class collaboration, *digits* supports the discovery and application of structure as a means for deepening understanding of a mathematical context. Featuring Understanding by Design as the pedagogical framework, *digits* asks students consistently to connect what they are learning to prior knowledge and construct content relationships. Focus on mathematical properties and their application through successive topics provides extensive transferability opportunities. Students gain deep understanding of the structure behind the properties with concrete patterns before making general, abstract conclusions.

8 Look for and express regularity in repeated reasoning.

Mathematically proficient students notice if calculations are repeated, and look both for general methods and for shortcuts. Upper elementary students might notice when dividing 25 by 11 that they are repeating the same calculations over and over again, and conclude they have a repeating decimal. By paying attention to the calculation of slope as they repeatedly check whether points are on the line through (1, 2) with slope 3, middle school students might abstract the equation $\frac{(y - 2)}{(x - 1)} = 3$. Noticing the regularity in the way terms cancel when expanding $(x - 1)(x + 1)$, $(x - 1)(x^2 + x + 1)$, and $(x - 1)(x^3 + x^2 + x + 1)$ might lead them to the general formula for the sum of a geometric series. As they work to solve a problem, mathematically proficient students maintain oversight of the process, while attending to the details. They continually evaluate the reasonableness of their intermediate results.

The Understanding by Design pedagogical framework of *digits* exposes students to a regularity and "sameness" of reasoning across topics and grades. Special features called "Know/Need/Plan" and "Think/Write" highlight how the same type of reasoning is applicable in many different mathematical contexts. Mathematical content in the program is grounded in ratio and proportion with concrete representations in grade 6 that evolve with repeated reasoning for Algebraic constructs in grade 8.

Grade 6 Lesson Correlation

Number	Standard for Mathematical Content	Lesson(s)
6.RP Ratios and Proportional Relationships		
Understand ratio concepts and use ratio reasoning to solve problems.		
6.RP.1	Understand the concept of a ratio and use ratio language to describe a ratio relationship between two quantities.	10-1 thru 10-6
6.RP.2	Understand the concept of a unit rate $\frac{a}{b}$ associated with a ratio $a : b$ with $b \neq 0$, and use rate language in the context of a ratio relationship.	11-1 thru 11-6, 12-2
6.RP.3	Use ratio and rate reasoning to solve real-world and mathematical problems, e.g., by reasoning about tables of equivalent ratios, tape diagrams, double number line diagrams, or equations.	10-6, 11-6, 12-5
6.RP.3a	Make tables of equivalent ratios relating quantities with whole number measurements, find missing values in the tables, and plot the pairs of values on the coordinate plane. Use tables to compare ratios.	10-2, 10-3, 12-1, 12-2
6.RP.3b	Solve unit rate problems including those involving unit pricing and constant speed.	11-2, 11-3
6.RP.3c	Find a percent of a quantity as a rate per 100 (e.g., 30% of a quantity means $\frac{30}{100}$ times the quantity); solve problems involving finding the whole, given a part and the percent.	12-3, 12-4, 12-5
6.RP.3d	Use ratio reasoning to convert measurement units; manipulate and transform units appropriately when multiplying or dividing quantities.	11-4
6.NS The Number System		
Apply and extend previous understandings of multiplication and division to divide fractions by fractions.		
6.NS.1	Interpret and compute quotients of fractions, and solve word problems involving division of fractions by fractions, e.g., by using visual fraction models and equations to represent the problem.	Topics 5 and 6
Compute fluently with multi-digit numbers and find common factors and multiples.		
6.NS.2	Fluently divide multi-digit numbers using the standard algorithm.	7-3, 7-4
6.NS.3	Fluently add, subtract, multiply, and divide multi-digit decimals using the standard algorithm for each operation.	7-1, 7-2, 7-3, 7-4
6.NS.4	Find the greatest common factor of two whole numbers less than or equal to 100 and the least common multiple of two whole numbers less than or equal to 12. Use the distributive property to express a sum of two whole numbers 1–100 with a common factor as a multiple of a sum of two whole numbers with no common factor.	2-4 thru 2-7

Number	Standard for Mathematical Content	Lesson(s)

6.NS The Number System (continued)

Apply and extend previous understandings of numbers to the system of rational numbers.

6.NS.5	Understand that positive and negative numbers are used together to describe quantities having opposite directions or values; use positive and negative numbers to represent quantities in real-world contexts, explaining the meaning of 0 in each situation.	8-1, 9-1
6.NS.6	Understand a rational number as a point on the number line. Extend number line diagrams and coordinate axes familiar from previous grades to represent points on the line and in the plane with negative number coordinates.	8-1, 8-4, 9-1, 9-2, 9-3, 9-4
6.NS.6a	Recognize opposite signs of numbers as indicating locations on opposite sides of 0 on the number line; recognize that the opposite of the opposite of a number is the number itself.	8-1, 9-1
6.NS.6b	Understand signs of numbers in ordered pairs as indicating locations in quadrants of the coordinate plane; recognize that when two ordered pairs differ only by signs, the locations of the points are related by reflections across one or both axes.	8-4, 9-4, 9-6
6.NS.6c	Find and position integers and other rational numbers on a horizontal or vertical number line diagram; find and position pairs of integers and other rational numbers on a coordinate plane.	8-1, 8-2, 8-4, 9-1, 9-3, 9-4
6.NS.7	Understand ordering and absolute value of rational numbers.	8-3, 9-3
6.NS.7a	Interpret statements of inequality as statements about the relative position of two numbers on a number line diagram.	8-2, 9-2, 9-3
6.NS.7b	Write, interpret, and explain statements of order for rational numbers in real-world contexts.	8-2, 9-2, 9-3, 9-6
6.NS.7c	Understand the absolute value of a rational number as its distance from 0 on the number line; interpret absolute value as magnitude for a positive or negative quantity in a real-world situation.	8-3, 8-6, 9-2, 9-3
6.NS.7d	Distinguish comparisons of absolute value from statements about order.	8-3, 9-3
6.NS.8	Solve real-world and mathematical problems by graphing points in all four quadrants of the coordinate plane. Include use of coordinates and absolute value to find distances between points with the same first coordinate or the same second coordinate.	4-2, 8-4, 8-5

6.EE Expressions and Equations

Apply and extend previous understandings of arithmetic to algebraic expressions.

6.EE.1	Write and evaluate numerical expressions involving whole-number exponents.	1-5
6.EE.2	Write, read, and evaluate expressions in which letters stand for numbers.	1-3, 1-4
6.EE.2a	Write expressions that record operations with numbers and with letters standing for numbers.	1-2, 1-3, 2-1, 2-2

Number	Standard for Mathematical Content	Lesson(s)
6.EE	**Expressions and Equations** *(continued)*	
Apply and extend previous understandings of arithmetic to algebraic expressions.		
6.EE.2b	Identify parts of an expression using mathematical terms (sum, term, product, factor, quotient, coefficient); view one or more parts of an expression as a single entity.	1-2, 2-1, 2-2, 2-3, 2-5, 2-6
6.EE.2c	Evaluate expressions at specific values of their variables. Include expressions that arise from formulas used in real-world problems. Perform arithmetic operations, including those involving whole number exponents, in the conventional order when there are no parentheses to specify a particular order (Order of Operations).	1-4, 1-5, 1-6
6.EE.3	Apply the properties of operations to generate equivalent expressions.	Topic 2
6.EE.4	Identify when two expressions are equivalent (i.e., when the two expressions name the same number regardless of which value is substituted into them).	1-1, 2-1, 2-2, 3-1
Reason about and solve one-variable equations and inequalities.		
6.EE.5	Understand solving an equation or inequality as a process of answering a question: which values from a specified set, if any, make the equation or inequality true? Use substitution to determine whether a given number in a specified set makes an equation or inequality true.	3-1, 3-2, 3-6, 3-7
6.EE.6	Use variables to represent numbers and write expressions when solving a real-world or mathematical problem; understand that a variable can represent an unknown number, or, depending on the purpose at hand, any number in a specified set.	1-2, 1-3
6.EE.7	Solve real-world and mathematical problems by writing and solving equations of the form $x + p = q$ and $px = q$ for cases in which p, q, and x are all nonnegative rational numbers.	3-3, 3-4, 3-7
6.EE.8	Write an inequality of the form $x > c$ or $x < c$ to represent a constraint or condition in a real-world or mathematical problem. Recognize that inequalities of the form $x > c$ or $x < c$ have infinitely many solutions; represent solutions of such inequalities on number line diagrams.	3-5, 3-6, 3-7
Represent and analyze quantitative relationships between dependent and independent variables.		
6.EE.9	Use variables to represent two quantities in a real-world problem that change in relationship to one another; write an equation to express one quantity, thought of as the dependent variable, in terms of the other quantity, thought of as the independent variable. Analyze the relationship between the dependent and independent variables using graphs and tables, and relate these to the equation.	4-1, 4-2, 4-3, 4-4, 12-1
6.G	**Geometry**	
Solve real-world and mathematical problems involving area, surface area, and volume.		
6.G.1	Find the area of right triangles, other triangles, special quadrilaterals, and polygons by composing into rectangles or decomposing into triangles and other shapes; apply these techniques in the context of solving real-world and mathematical problems.	13-1, 13-2, 13-3, 13-4, 13-5, 13-6

Number	Standard for Mathematical Content	Lesson(s)

6.G Geometry (continued)

Solve real-world and mathematical problems involving area, surface area, and volume.

Number	Standard for Mathematical Content	Lesson(s)
6.G.2	Find the volume of a right rectangular prism with fractional edge lengths by packing it with unit cubes of the appropriate unit fraction edge lengths, and show that the volume is the same as would be found by multiplying the edge lengths of the prism. Apply the formulas $V = lwh$ and $V = bh$ to find volumes of right rectangular prisms with fractional edge lengths in the context of solving real-world and mathematical problems.	14-5, 14-6
6.G.3	Draw polygons in the coordinate plane given coordinates for the vertices; use coordinates to find the length of a side joining points with the same first coordinate or the same second coordinate. Apply these techniques in the context of solving real-world and mathematical problems.	8-5, 8-6, 9-5, 9-6
6.G.4	Represent three-dimensional figures using nets made up of rectangles and triangles, and use the nets to find the surface area of these figures. Apply these techniques in the context of solving real-world and mathematical problems.	14-1, 14-2, 14-3, 14-4, 14-6

6.SP Statistics and Probability

Develop understanding of statistical variability.

Number	Standard for Mathematical Content	Lesson(s)
6.SP.1	Recognize a statistical question as one that anticipates variability in the data related to the question and accounts for it in the answers.	15-1, 15-6
6.SP.2	Understand that a set of data collected to answer a statistical question has a distribution which can be described by its center, spread, and overall shape.	15-2, 15-3, 16-2, 16-3
6.SP.3	Recognize that a measure of center for a numerical data set summarizes all of its values with a single number, while a measure of variation describes how its values vary with a single number.	16-1, 16-2, 16-3, 16-4, 16-5, 16-6

Summarize and describe distributions.

Number	Standard for Mathematical Content	Lesson(s)
6.SP.4	Display numerical data in plots on a number line, including dot plots, histograms, and box plots.	15-2, 15-3, 15-4
6.SP.5	Summarize numerical data sets in relation to their context, such as by:	15-6, 16-6
6.SP.5a	Reporting the number of observations.	15-6
6.SP.5b	Describing the nature of the attribute under investigation, including how it was measured and its units of measurement.	15-1
6.SP.5c	Giving quantitative measures of center (median and/or mean) and variability (interquartile range and/or mean absolute deviation), as well as describing any overall pattern and any striking deviations from the overall pattern with reference to the context in which the data were gathered.	16-1, 16-2, 16-3, 16-4, 16-5, 16-6
6.SP.5.d	Summarize numerical data sets in relation to their context, such as by: Relating the choice of measures of center and variability to the shape of the data distribution and the context in which the data were gathered.	16-1, 16-2, 16-3, 16-4, 16-5, 16-6

Grade 7 Lesson Correlation

Number	Standard for Mathematical Content	Lesson(s)
7.RP Ratios and Proportional Relationships		
Analyze proportional relationships and use them to solve real-world and mathematical problems.		
7.RP.1	Compute unit rates associated with ratios of fractions, including ratios of lengths, areas and other quantities measured in like or different units.	1-1, 1-2, 1-3, 1-4, 1-5
7.RP.2	Recognize and represent proportional relationships between quantities.	2-1, 2-2, 2-3, 2-4, 2-6, 3-1, 3-2, 3-3, 3-5
7.RP.2.a	Decide whether two quantities are in a proportional relationship, e.g., by testing for equivalent ratios in a table or graphing on a coordinate plane and observing whether the graph is a straight line through the origin.	2-1, 2-2, 2-6
7.RP.2.b	Identify the constant of proportionality (unit rate) in tables, graphs, equations, diagrams, and verbal descriptions of proportional relationships.	2-3, 2-6, 3-1
7.RP.2.c	Represent proportional relationships by equations.	2-4, 2-6, 3-1
7.RP.2.d	Explain what a point (x, y) on the graph of a proportional relationship means in terms of the situation, with special attention to the points $(0, 0)$ and $(1, r)$ where r is the unit rate.	2-2, 2-3, 2-6
7.RP.3	Use proportional relationships to solve multistep ratio and percent problems. Examples: simple interest, tax, markups and markdowns, gratuities and commissions, fees, percent increase and decrease, percent error.	3-2, 3-3, 3-5, 3-6, 3-7
7.NS The Number System		
Apply and extend previous understandings of operations with fractions to add, subtract, multiply, and divide rational numbers.		
7.NS.1	Apply and extend previous understandings of addition and subtraction to add and subtract rational numbers; represent addition and subtraction on a horizontal or vertical number line diagram.	4-1, 4-2, 4-4, 4-5
7.NS.1.a	Describe situations in which opposite quantities combine to make 0. For example, a hydrogen atom has 0 charge because its two constituents are oppositely charged.	4-1
7.NS.1.b	Understand $p + q$ as the number located a distance $\|q\|$ from p, in the positive or negative direction depending on whether q is positive or negative. Show that a number and its opposite have a sum of 0 (are additive inverses). Interpret sums of rational numbers by describing real-world contexts.	4-2, 4-3, 4-5, 4-7
7.NS.1.c	Understand subtraction of rational numbers as adding the additive inverse, $p - q = p + (-q)$. Show that the distance between two rational numbers on the number line is the absolute value of their difference, and apply this principle in real-world contexts.	4-4, 4-6, 4-7

Number	Standard for Mathematical Content	Lesson(s)

7.NS The Number System (continued)

Apply and extend previous understandings of operations with fractions to add, subtract, multiply, and divide rational numbers.

Number	Standard for Mathematical Content	Lesson(s)
7.NS.1.d	Apply properties of operations as strategies to add and subtract rational numbers.	4-3
7.NS.2	Apply and extend previous understandings of multiplication and division and of fractions to multiply and divide rational numbers.	5-1, 5-2, 5-3, 5-4, 5-5
7.NS.2.a	Understand that multiplication is extended from fractions to rational numbers by requiring that operations continue to satisfy the properties of operations, particularly the distributive property, leading to products such as $(-1)(-1) = 1$ and the rules for multiplying signed numbers. Interpret products of rational numbers by describing real-world contexts.	5-1, 5-2
7.NS.2.b	Understand that integers can be divided, provided that the divisor is not zero, and every quotient of integers (with non-zero divisor) is a rational number. If p and q are integers, then $\left(\frac{p}{q}\right) = \frac{(-p)}{q} = \frac{p}{(-q)}$. Interpret quotients of rational numbers by describing real-world contexts.	5-3, 5-4, 6-1, 6-2, 6-5
7.NS.2.c	Apply properties of operations as strategies to multiply and divide rational numbers.	5-1, 5-5
7.NS.2.d	Convert a rational number to a decimal using long division; know that the decimal form of a rational number terminates in 0s or eventually repeats.	6-1, 6-2, 6-5
7.NS.3	Solve real-world and mathematical problems involving the four operations with rational numbers.	5-5, 6-3, 6-4, 6-5

7.EE Expressions and Equations

Use properties of operations to generate equivalent expressions.

Number	Standard for Mathematical Content	Lesson(s)
7.EE.1	Apply properties of operations as strategies to add, subtract, factor, and expand linear expressions with rational coefficients.	7-1, 7-2, 7-3, 7-4, 7-5
7.EE.2	Understand that rewriting an expression in different forms in a problem context can shed light on the problem and how the quantities in it are related. For example, $a + 0.05a = 1.05a$ means that "increase by 5%" is the same as "multiply by 1.05."	7-1, 7-2, 7-3, 7-4, 7-5

Solve real-life and mathematical problems using numerical and algebraic expressions and equations.

Number	Standard for Mathematical Content	Lesson(s)
7.EE.3	Solve multi-step real-life and mathematical problems posed with positive and negative rational numbers in any form (whole numbers, fractions, and decimals), using tools strategically. Apply properties of operations to calculate with numbers in any form; convert between forms as appropriate; and assess the reasonableness of answers using mental computation and estimation strategies.	4-7, 5-6, 8-3, 8-4, 8-5
7.EE.4	Use variables to represent quantities in a real-world or mathematical problem, and construct simple equations and inequalities to solve problems by reasoning about the quantities.	8-1, 8-2, 8-3, 8-4, 8-5, 9-1, 9-2, 9-3, 9-4, 9-5, 10-1, 11-1

Number	Standard for Mathematical Content	Lesson(s)
7.EE Expressions and Equations (*continued*)		
Solve real-life and mathematical problems using numerical and algebraic expressions and equations.		
7.EE.4.a	Solve word problems leading to equations of the form $px + q = r$ and $p(x + q) = r$, where p, q, and r are specific rational numbers. Solve equations of these forms fluently. Compare an algebraic solution to an arithmetic solution, identifying the sequence of the operations used in each approach.	8-1, 8-2, 8-3, 8-4, 8-5, 10-1, 11-1
7.EE.4.b	Solve word problems leading to inequalities of the form $px + q > r$ or $px + q < r$, where p, q, and r are specific rational numbers. Graph the solution set of the inequality and interpret it in the context of the problem.	9-1, 9-2, 9-3, 9-4, 9-5
7.G Geometry		
Draw construct, and describe geometrical figures and describe the relationships between them.		
7.G.1	Solve problems involving scale drawings of geometric figures, including computing actual lengths and areas from a scale drawing and reproducing a scale drawing at a different scale.	2-5, 2-6
7.G.2	Draw (freehand, with ruler and protractor, and with technology) geometric shapes with given conditions. Focus on constructing triangles from three measures of angles or sides, noticing when the conditions determine a unique triangle, more than one triangle, or no triangle.	10-1, 10-2, 10-3, 10-4, 10-5, 11-1, 11-2, 11-3, 12-1, 12-2, 12-3, 12-6
7.G.3	Describe the two-dimensional figures that result from slicing three- dimensional figures, as in plane sections of right rectangular prisms and right rectangular pyramids.	12-6
Solve real-life and mathematical problems involving angle measure, area, surface area, and volume.		
7.G.4	Know the formulas for the area and circumference of a circle and use them to solve problems; give an informal derivation of the relationship between the circumference and area of a circle.	11-1, 11-2, 11-3, 11-4, 11-5
7.G.5	Use facts about supplementary, complementary, vertical, and adjacent angles in a multi-step problem to write and solve simple equations for an unknown angle in a figure.	10-2, 10-3, 10-4, 10-5, 10-6
7.G.6	Solve real-world and mathematical problems involving area, volume and surface area of two- and three-dimensional objects composed of triangles, quadrilaterals, polygons, cubes, and right prisms.	12-6, 13-1, 13-2, 13-3, 13-4, 13-5
7.SP Statistics and Probability		
Use random sampling to draw inferences about a population.		
7.SP.1	Understand that statistics can be used to gain information about a population by examining a sample of the population; generalizations about a population from a sample are valid only if the sample is representative of that population. Understand that random sampling tends to produce representative samples and support valid inferences.	14-1, 14-2, 14-3, 14-4, 14-5, 14-6, 14-7, 15-1, 15-2

Number	Standard for Mathematical Content	Lesson(s)

7.SP Statistics and Probability (continued)

Use random sampling to draw inferences about a population.

Number	Standard for Mathematical Content	Lesson(s)
7.SP.2	Use data from a random sample to draw inferences about a population with an unknown characteristic of interest. Generate multiple samples (or simulated samples) of the same size to gauge the variation in estimates or predictions.	14-2, 14-5, 14-7

Draw informal comparative inferences about two populations.

Number	Standard for Mathematical Content	Lesson(s)
7.SP.3	Informally assess the degree of visual overlap of two numerical data distributions with similar variabilities, measuring the difference between the centers by expressing it as a multiple of a measure of variability.	15-2, 15-5
7.SP.4	Use measures of center and measures of variability for numerical data from random samples to draw informal comparative inferences about two populations.	15-1, 15-2, 15-3, 15-4, 15-5, 15-6

Investigate chance processes and develop, use, and evaluate probability models.

Number	Standard for Mathematical Content	Lesson(s)
7.SP.5	Understand that the probability of a chance event is a number between 0 and 1 that expresses the likelihood of the event occurring. Larger numbers indicate greater likelihood. A probability near 0 indicates an unlikely event, a probability around $\frac{1}{2}$ indicates an event that is neither unlikely nor likely, and a probability near 1 indicates a likely event.	16-1
7.SP.6	Approximate the probability of a chance event by collecting data on the chance process that produces it and observing its long-run relative frequency, and predict the approximate relative frequency given the probability.	16-1, 16-3, 17-4
7.SP.7	Develop a probability model and use it to find probabilities of events. Compare probabilities from a model to observed frequencies; if the agreement is not good, explain possible sources of the discrepancy.	16-2, 16-4, 16-5, 16-6, 17-7
7.SP.7.a	Develop a uniform probability model by assigning equal probability to all outcomes, and use the model to determine probabilities of events.	16-4, 16-5, 16-6
7.SP.7.b	Develop a probability model (which may not be uniform) by observing frequencies in data generated from a chance process.	16-5, 16-6
7.SP.8	Find probabilities of compound events using organized lists, tables, tree diagrams, and simulation.	17-1, 17-2, 17-3, 17-4, 17-5, 17-6, 17-7
7.SP.8.a	Understand that, just as with simple events, the probability of a compound event is the fraction of outcomes in the sample space for which the compound event occurs.	17-3, 17-4
7.SP.8.b	Represent sample spaces for compound events using methods such as organized lists, tables and tree diagrams. For an event described in everyday language (e.g., "rolling double sixes"), identify the outcomes in the sample space which compose the event.	17-1, 17-2, 17-3
7.SP.8.c	Design and use a simulation to generate frequencies for compound events. For example, use random digits as a simulation tool to approximate the answer to the question: If 40% of donors have type A blood, what is the probability that it will take at least 4 donors to find one with type A blood?	17-5

Grade 8 Lesson Correlation

Number	Standard for Mathematical Content	Lesson(s)

8.NS   The Number System

Know that there are numbers that are not rational, and approximate them by rational numbers.

Number	Standard for Mathematical Content	Lesson(s)
8.NS.1	Know that numbers that are not rational are called irrational. Understand informally that every number has a decimal expansion; for rational numbers show that the decimal expansion repeats eventually, and convert a decimal expansion which repeats eventually into a rational number.	1-1, 1-2, 1-5
8.NS.2	Use rational approximations of irrational numbers to compare the size of irrational numbers, locate them approximately on a number line diagram, and estimate the value of expressions (e.g., π^2). For example, by truncating the decimal expansion of $\sqrt{2}$, show that $\sqrt{2}$ is between 1 and 2, then between 1.4 and 1.5, and explain how to continue on to get better approximations.	1-3, 1-4, 1-5

8.EE   Expressions and Equations

Work with radicals and integer exponents.

Number	Standard for Mathematical Content	Lesson(s)
8.EE.1	Know and apply the properties of integer exponents to generate equivalent numerical expressions. For example, $3^2 \times 3^{(-5)} = 3^{(-3)} = \frac{1}{(3^3)} = \frac{1}{27}$.	3-3, 3-4, 3-5, 3-6, 3-7, 4-5
8.EE.2	Use square root and cube root symbols to represent solutions to equations of the form $x^2 = p$ and $x^3 = p$, where p is a positive rational number. Evaluate square roots of small perfect squares and cube roots of small perfect cubes. Know that $\sqrt{2}$ is irrational.	3-1, 3-2
8.EE.3	Use numbers expressed in the form of a single digit times an integer power of 10 to estimate very large or very small quantities, and to express how many times as much one is than the other. For example, estimate the population of the United States as 3×10^8 and the population of the world as 7×10^9, and determine that the world population is more than 20 times larger.	4-1, 4-2, 4-3, 4-4
8.EE.4	Perform operations with numbers expressed in scientific notation, including problems where both decimal and scientific notation are used. Use scientific notation and choose units of appropriate size for measurements of very large or very small quantities (e.g., use millimeters per year for seafloor spreading). Interpret scientific notation that has been generated by technology.	4-1, 4-4, 4-5

Understand the connections between proportional relationships, lines, and linear equations.

Number	Standard for Mathematical Content	Lesson(s)
8.EE.5	Graph proportional relationships, interpreting the unit rate as the slope of the graph. Compare two different proportional relationships represented in different ways. For example, compare a distance-time graph to a distance-time equation to determine which of two moving objects has greater speed.	5-1, 5-2, 5-3, 5-4, 5-7
8.EE.6	Use similar triangles to explain why the slope m is the same between any two distinct points on a non-vertical line in the coordinate plane; derive the equation $y = mx$ for a line through the origin and the equation $y = mx + b$ for a line intercepting the vertical axis at b.	5-2, 5-5, 5-6, 5-7, 10-3

Number	Standard for Mathematical Content	Lesson(s)

8.EE Expressions and Equations (continued)

Analyze and solve linear equations and pairs of simultaneous linear equations.

Number	Standard for Mathematical Content	Lesson(s)
8.EE.7	Solve linear equations in one variable.	2-1, 2-2, 2-4, 2-5
8.EE.7.a	Give examples of linear equations in one variable with one solution, infinitely many solutions, or no solutions. Show which of these possibilities is the case by successively transforming the given equation into simpler forms, until an equivalent equation of the form $x = a$, $a = a$, or $a = b$ results (where a and b are different numbers).	2-4, 2-5
8.EE.7.b	Solve linear equations with rational number coefficients, including equations whose solutions require expanding expressions using the distributive property and collecting like terms.	2-1, 2-2, 2-3
8.EE.8	Analyze and solve pairs of simultaneous linear equations.	6-1, 6-2, 6-4, 6-5, 6-6, 6-7
8.EE.8.a	Understand that solutions to a system of two linear equations in two variables correspond to points of intersection of their graphs, because points of intersection satisfy both equations simultaneously.	6-1, 6-3, 6-5, 6-6
8.EE.8.b	Solve systems of two linear equations in two variables algebraically, and estimate solutions by graphing the equations. Solve simple cases by inspection. For example, $3x + 2y = 5$ and $3x + 2y = 6$ have no solution because $3x + 2y$ cannot simultaneously be 5 and 6.	6-2, 6-3, 6-4, 6-5, 6-6, 6-7
8.EE.8.c	Solve real-world and mathematical problems leading to two linear equations in two variables. For example, given coordinates for two pairs of points, determine whether the line through the first pair of points intersects the line through the second pair.	6-1, 6-3, 6-4, 6-5, 6-6, 6-7

8.F Functions

Define, evaluate, and compare functions.

Number	Standard for Mathematical Content	Lesson(s)
8.F.1	Understand that a function is a rule that assigns to each input exactly one output. The graph of a function is the set of ordered pairs consisting of an input and the corresponding output.	7-1, 7-2, 7-4, 8-1
8.F.2	Compare properties of two functions each represented in a different way (algebraically, graphically, numerically in tables, or by verbal descriptions). For example, given a linear function represented by a table of values and a linear function represented by an algebraic expression, determine which function has the greater rate of change.	8-4
8.F.3	Interpret the equation $y = mx + b$ as defining a linear function, whose graph is a straight line; give examples of functions that are not linear. For example, the function $A = s^2$ giving the area of a square as a function of its side length is not linear because its graph contains the points (1,1), (2,4) and (3,9), which are not on a straight line.	7-3, 7-4, 8-1, 8-3

Number	Standard for Mathematical Content	Lesson(s)
8.F	**Functions** *(continued)*	

Use functions to model relationships between quantities.

Number	Standard for Mathematical Content	Lesson(s)
8.F.4	Construct a function to model a linear relationship between two quantities. Determine the rate of change and initial value of the function from a description of a relationship or from two (x, y) values, including reading these from a table or from a graph. Interpret the rate of change and initial value of a linear function in terms of the situation it models, and in terms of its graph or a table of values.	8-1, 8-2, 8-3, 8-5, 8-6
8.F.5	Describe qualitatively the functional relationship between two quantities by analyzing a graph (e.g., where the function is increasing or decreasing, linear or nonlinear). Sketch a graph that exhibits the qualitative features of a function that has been described verbally.	7-3, 7-4, 7-5, 7-6, 7-7, 8-1, 8-2, 8-3

Number	Standard for Mathematical Content	Lesson(s)
8.G	**Geometry**	

Understand congruence and similarity using physical models, transparencies, or geometry software.

Number	Standard for Mathematical Content	Lesson(s)
8.G.1	Verify experimentally the properties of rotations, reflections, and translations:	9-1, 9-2, 9-3, 10-1
8.G.1.a	Verify experimentally the properties of rotations, reflections, and translations: Lines are taken to lines, and line segments to line segments of the same length.	9-1, 9-2, 9-3
8.G.1.b	Verify experimentally the properties of rotations, reflections, and translations: Angles are taken to angles of the same measure.	9-1, 9-2, 9-3
8.G.1.c	Verify experimentally the properties of rotations, reflections, and translations: Parallel lines are taken to parallel lines.	9-1, 9-2, 9-3
8.G.2	Understand that a two-dimensional figure is congruent to another if the second can be obtained from the first by a sequence of rotations, reflections, and translations; given two congruent figures, describe a sequence that exhibits the congruence between them.	9-4, 9-5
8.G.3	Describe the effect of dilations, translations, rotations, and reflections on two-dimensional figures using coordinates.	10-1, 10-2, 10-3, 10-4
8.G.4	Understand that a two-dimensional figure is similar to another if the second can be obtained from the first by a sequence of rotations, reflections, translations, and dilations; given two similar two- dimensional figures, describe a sequence that exhibits the similarity between them.	10-2, 10-3, 10-4, 11-5
8.G.5	Use informal arguments to establish facts about the angle sum and exterior angle of triangles, about the angles created when parallel lines are cut by a transversal, and the angle-angle criterion for similarity of triangles.	11-1, 11-2, 11-3, 11-4, 11-5, 11-6

Number	Standard for Mathematical Content	Lesson(s)

8.G Geometry (continued)

Understand and apply the Pythagorean Theorem.

Number	Standard for Mathematical Content	Lesson(s)
8.G.6	Explain a proof of the Pythagorean Theorem and its converse.	12-1, 12-2, 12-4
8.G.7	Apply the Pythagorean Theorem to determine unknown side lengths in right triangles in real-world and mathematical problems in two and three dimensions.	12-2, 12-3, 12-6
8.G.8	Apply the Pythagorean Theorem to find the distance between two points in a coordinate system.	12-5, 12-6

Solve real-world and mathematical problems involving volume of cylinders, cones, and spheres.

Number	Standard for Mathematical Content	Lesson(s)
8.G.9	Know the formulas for the volumes of cones, cylinders, and spheres and use them to solve real-world and mathematical problems.	13-1, 13-2, 13-3, 13-4, 13-5, 13-6, 13-7

8.SP Statistics and Probability

Investigate patterns of association in bivariate data.

Number	Standard for Mathematical Content	Lesson(s)
8.SP.1	Construct and interpret scatter plots for bivariate measurement data to investigate patterns of association between two quantities. Describe patterns such as clustering, outliers, positive or negative association, linear association, and nonlinear association.	14-1, 14-2, 14-3, 14-4
8.SP.2	Know that straight lines are widely used to model relationships between two quantitative variables. For scatter plots that suggest a linear association, informally fit a straight line, and informally assess the model fit by judging the closeness of the data points to the line.	14-5, 14-6, 14-7
8.SP.3	Use the equation of a linear model to solve problems in the context of bivariate measurement data, interpreting the slope and intercept.	14-6
8.SP.4	Understand that patterns of association can also be seen in bivariate categorical data by displaying frequencies and relative frequencies in a two-way table. Construct and interpret a two-way table summarizing data on two categorical variables collected from the same subjects. Use relative frequencies calculated for rows or columns to describe possible association between the two variables.	15-1, 15-2, 15-3, 15-4, 15-5, 15-6, 15-7

Intervention Scope and Sequence

Intervention Lessons	Use With Grade			Prerequisite for Units	CCSSM
	6	7	8		
Cluster 1: Place Value					
Lesson 1: Place Value	☑	☑	☑	6A, 7E	4.NBT1, 4.NBT2
Lesson 2: Comparing and Ordering Whole Numbers	☑	☑	☑	6A, 6F	4.NBT2
Cluster 2: Multiplication Number Sense					
Lesson 1: Addition and Multiplication Properties	☑	☑	☑	6A, 7C	3.OA5
Lesson 2: Distributive Property	☑	☑	☑	6A, 7C	3.OA5, 3.MD7
Lesson 3: Multiplying by Multiples of 10, 100, and 1,000	☑	☑	☑	6A	5.NBT2
Lesson 4: Using Mental Math to Multiply	☑	☑	☑	6B, 6D	3.OA5
Lesson 5: Estimating Products	☑	☑	☑	6A	4.OA3
Cluster 3: Multiplying Whole Numbers					
Lesson 1: Multiplying by 1-Digit Numbers: Expanded	☑	☑	☑	6A	4NBT3, 4NBT5
Lesson 2: Multiplying by 1-Digit Numbers	☑	☑	☑	6A, 6B, 6E	4NBT5
Lesson 3: Using Patterns to Multiply and Estimate	☑	☑	☑	6C, 6E	4.OA3, 5.NBT2
Lesson 4: Multiplying by 2-Digit Numbers: Expanded	☑	☑	☑	6C, 6E	4NBT5, 5NBT5
Lesson 5: Multiplying by 2-Digit Numbers	☑	☑	☑	6C, 6E	4NBT5, 5NBT5
Cluster 4: Dividing by 1-Digit Numbers					
Lesson 1: Dividing Multiples of 10 and 100	☑	☑	☑	6A, 6D, 6F	4.NBT6, 4.OA3
Lesson 2: Estimating Quotients with 1-Digit Divisors	☑	☑	☑	6A	4.OA3
Lesson 3: Dividing: 1-Digit Divisors, 2-Digit Dividends	☑	☑	☑	6A, 6D, 6F, 7E	4.NBT6
Lesson 4: Dividing: 1-Digit Divisors, 3-Digit Dividends	☑	☑	☑	6A, 6D, 6F	4NBT6
Lesson 5: Dividing: 1-Digit Divisors, 4-Digit Dividends	☑	☑	☑	6F	4NBT6
Lesson 6: Divisibility Rules	☑	☑	☑	6A, 6B, 7F	4.OA4
Cluster 5: Dividing by 2-Digit Numbers					
Lesson 1: Using Patterns to Divide	☑	☑	☑	6C, 6F	5.NBT6
Lesson 2: Estimating Quotients with 2-Digit Divisors	☑	☑	☑	6F	5.NBT6, 4.OA3
Lesson 3: Dividing: 2-Digit Divisors, 1-Digit Quotients	☑	☑	☑	6C, 6F, 7E	5.NBT6
Lesson 4: Dividing: 2-Digit Divisors, 2-Digit Quotients	☑	☑	☑	6C, 6F, 7E	5.NBT6
Cluster 6: Decimal Number Sense					
Lesson 1: Understanding Decimals	☑	☑	☑	6C, 6D, 6F	4.NF6, 5.NBT1, 5.NBT3
Lesson 2: Comparing and Ordering Decimals	☑	☑	☑	6C, 6F, 7E	4.NF7, 5.NBT3
Lesson 3: Rounding Decimals	☑	☑	☑	6C, 6D	5.NBT4

Intervention Lessons	Use With Grade			Prerequisite for Units	CCSSM
	6	7	8		
Cluster 7: Adding and Subtracting Decimals					
Lesson 1: Estimating Sums and Differences of Decimals	☑	☑	☑	6C, 6F	5.NBT7
Lesson 2: Adding and Subtracting Decimals	☑	☑	☑	6C, 6F	5.NBT7
Cluster 8: Multiplying and Dividing Decimals					
Lesson 1: Patterns in Multiplying and Dividing Decimals		☑	☑	7A, 8F	5.NBT2
Lesson 2: Multiplying Decimals	☑	☑	☑	6D, 6E, 7B, 7D, 7E, 7F, 8E, 8F	5.NBT7
Lesson 3: Dividing Decimals by Whole Numbers	☑	☑	☑	6C, 6D, 6F, 7B, 7E, 8F	5.NBT7
Lesson 4: Estimating Decimal Products and Quotients	☑	☑	☑	6D	5.NBT7, 7.EE3
Lesson 5: Dividing Decimals		☑	☑	7A, 7E, 8F	5.NBT7, 6.NS3
Cluster 9: Fraction Number Sense					
Lesson 1: Equivalent Fractions	☑	☑	☑	6B, 6D, 7A, 7F, 8F	4.NF1
Lesson 2: Fractions in Simplest Form	☑	☑	☑	6B, 6D, 7A, 7F	4.NF1
Lesson 3: Comparing and Ordering Fractions	☑	☑	☑	6C, 7E, 7F, 8A	4.NF2
Lesson 4: Fractions and Division	☑	☑	☑	6B, 7B	5.NF3
Lesson 5: Fractions and Decimals	☑	☑	☑	6C, 6D, 7F, 8F	4.NF6
Cluster 10: Adding and Subtracting Fractions					
Lesson 1: Adding Fractions with Like Denominators	☑	☑	☑	7B	4.NF3
Lesson 2: Subtracting Fractions with Like Denominators	☑	☑	☑	7B	4.NF3
Lesson 3: Adding Fractions with Unlike Denominators	☑	☑	☑	7B	5.NF1, 5.NF2
Lesson 4: Subtracting with Unlike Denominators	☑	☑	☑	7B	5.NF1, 5.NF2
Cluster 11: Multiplying and Dividing Fractions					
Lesson 1: Multiplying a Whole Number and a Fraction	☑	☑	☑	6B, 6E, 7F	4.NF4, 5.NF4, 5.NF6
Lesson 2: Multiplying Fractions	☑	☑	☑	6B, 6E, 7A	5.NF4, 5.NF6
Lesson 3: Dividing a Unit Fraction by a Whole Number	☑	☑	☑	7B	5.NF7, 6.NS1
Lesson 4: Dividing a Whole Number by a Unit Fraction	☑	☑	☑	7B	5.NF7, 6.NS1
Lesson 5: Dividing Fractions		☑	☑	7B	6.NS1
Cluster 12: Mixed Numbers					
Lesson 1: Mixed Numbers and Improper Fractions	☑	☑	☑	6B, 6E, 7B	4.NF4, 5.NF6
Lesson 2: Adding Mixed Numbers	☑	☑	☑	7B	4.NF3, 5.NF1
Cluster 12: Mixed Numbers (continued)					
Lesson 3: Subtracting Mixed Numbers	☑	☑	☑	7B	4.NF3, 5.NF1
Lesson 4: Multiplying Mixed Numbers	☑	☑	☑	6B, 6E	5.NF6
Lesson 5: Dividing Mixed Numbers		☑	☑	8B	6.NS1, 7.NS3

Intervention Lessons	Use With Grade 6	Use With Grade 7	Use With Grade 8	Prerequisite for Units	CCSSM
Cluster 13: Ratios					
Lesson 1: Ratios		☑	☑	7A, 7F, 8D, 8F	6.RP1
Lesson 2: Equivalent Ratios		☑	☑	7A, 8D, 8F	6.RP3
Cluster 14: Rates and Measurements					
Lesson 1: Unit Rates		☑	☑	7A, 8C, 8D	6.RP2, 6.RP3B
Lesson 2: Converting Customary Measurements		☑	☑	7A	6.RP3
Lesson 3: Converting Metric Measurements		☑	☑	7A	6.RP3
Cluster 15: Proportional Relationships					
Lesson 1: Graphing Ratios		☑	☑	7A, 8C, 8D, 8F	6.RP3
Lesson 2: Recognizing Proportional Relationships			☑	8C, 8E	7.RP2
Lesson 3: Constant of Proportionality			☑	8E	7.RP2
Cluster 16: Number Sense with Percents					
Lesson 1: Understanding Percent		☑	☑	7A, 7E, 7F, 8F	6.RP3C
Lesson 2: Estimating Percent		☑	☑	7E, 7F	6.RP3C
Cluster 17: Computations with Percents					
Lesson 1: Finding a Percent of a Number		☑	☑	7A, 7E, 7F, 8F	6.RP3
Lesson 2: Finding a Percent		☑	☑	7E, 8F	6.RP3
Lesson 3: Finding the Whole Given a Percent		☑	☑	7E	6.RP3
Lesson 4: Sales Tax, Tips, and Simple Interest			☑	8C	7.RP3
Lesson 5: Markdowns			☑	8C	7.RP3
Cluster 18: Exponents					
Lesson 1: Exponents		☑	☑	7C, 7D, 8B, 8E	6.EE1, 5.NBT2
Lesson 2: Multiplying Decimals by Powers of Ten	☑	☑	☑	8B	5.NBT2
Cluster 19: Geometry					
Lesson 1: Classifying Triangles	☑	☑	☑	6E, 7D	4.G2, 5.G3, 5.G4
Lesson 2: Classifying Quadrilaterals	☑	☑	☑	6E, 7D	4.G2, 5.G3, 5.G4
Cluster 20: Measuring 2- and 3-Dimensional Objects					
Lesson 1: Perimeter	☑	☑	☑	6E	4.MD3
Lesson 2: Area of Rectangles and Squares	☑	☑	☑	6E, 7D, 8E	4.MD3
Lesson 3: Area of Parallelograms and Triangles		☑	☑	7D, 8E	6.G1
Cluster 20: Measuring 2- and 3-Dimensional Objects (continued)					
Lesson 4: Nets and Surface Area		☑	☑	7D, 8E	6.G3
Lesson 5: Volume of Prisms	☑	☑	☑	6E, 7D, 8E	5.MD3, 5.MD4, 5.MD5

Intervention Lessons	Use With Grade 6	7	8	Prerequisite for Units	CCSSM
Cluster 21: Integers					
Lesson 1: Understanding Integers		✓	✓	7B, 8A, 8D	6.NS5, 6.NS6, 6.NS7
Lesson 2: Comparing and Ordering Integers		✓	✓	8A	6.NS7
Lesson 3: Adding Integers			✓	8B	7.NS1
Lesson 4: Subtracting Integers			✓	8B	7.NS1
Lesson 5: Multiplying Integers			✓	8B	7.NS2
Lesson 6: Dividing Integers			✓	8B	7.NS2
Cluster 22: Graphing and Rational Numbers					
Lesson 1: Graphing in the First Quadrant	✓	✓	✓	6D, 7A, 8D, 8E, 8F	5.G1, 5.G2
Lesson 2: Graphing in the Coordinate Plane		✓	✓	8C, 8D, 8E, 8F	6.NS6
Lesson 3: Distance When There's a Common Coordinate		✓	✓	8E	6.G3
Lesson 4: Rational Numbers on the Number Line		✓	✓	8A	6.NS6
Lesson 5: Comparing and Ordering Rational Numbers		✓	✓	8A	6.NS7
Cluster 23: Numerical and Algebraic Expressions					
Lesson 1: Order of Operations	✓	✓	✓	7C, 7D, 8D, 8E	5.OA1, 6.EE2C
Lesson 2: Variables and Expressions		✓	✓	7C, 8D	6.EE2, 6.EE6
Lesson 3: Patterns and Expressions		✓	✓	8D, 8F	6.EE2, 6.EE6
Lesson 4: Evaluating Expressions: Whole Numbers		✓	✓	7D, 8D, 8E	6.EE2
Cluster 24: More Algebraic Expressions					
Lesson 1: Evaluating Expressions: Rational Numbers		✓	✓	8D, 8E	6.EE2
Lesson 2: Equivalent Expressions		✓	✓	7C, 8B, 8C	6.EE3, 6.EE4
Lesson 3: Simplifying Expressions		✓	✓	7C, 8B, 8C	6.EE3
Cluster 25: Equations					
Lesson 1: Writing Equations		✓	✓	7C, 8D	6.EE7
Lesson 2: Principles of Solving Equations		✓	✓	7C, 7D, 8B, 8C	6.EE5
Lesson 3: Solving Addition and Subtraction Equations		✓	✓	7C, 7D, 8B, 8C	6.EE7
Lesson 4: Solving Multiplication and Division Equations		✓	✓	7C, 8C	6.EE7
Lesson 5: Solving Rational-Number Equations, Part 1		✓	✓	8B, 8C	6.EE7
Lesson 6: Solving Rational-Number Equations, Part 2		✓	✓	8B, 8C	6.EE7
Lesson 7: Solving Two-Step Equations			✓	8C	7.EE4

Correlation of Readiness Assessments and Intervention Lessons

Three questions in each Readiness Assessment correlate to an Intervention Lesson. If a student submits an incorrect answer for two of the three questions, that Intervention Lesson is assigned in the student's Study Plan.

Readiness Assessment Grade 6

	CCSS Standard	Readiness Assessment Question Number	Assigned Intervention Lesson
6A	3.OA5, 2.NBT6	1, 8, 11	2-1
	4.NBT1, 4.NBT2	2, 6, 7	1-1
	3.OA5, 3.MD7	3, 12, 13	2-2
	4.NBT2	4, 5, 9	1-2
	4.OA3	10, 14, 16	2-5
	4.NBT5	15, 18, 19	3-2
	4.OA3	17, 20, 22	4-2
	4.NBT6	21, 23, 25	4-3
	4.NBT6	24, 26, 29	4-4
	4.OA4	27, 28, 30	4-6
6B	4.NBT5	1, 5, 6	3-2
	3.OA5	2, 4, 7	2-4
	4.OA4	3, 8, 10	4-6
	4.NF1	9, 11, 13	9-1
	4.NF1	12, 14, 16	9-2
	5.NF3	15, 17, 19	9-4
	4.NF4, 5.NF4, 5.NF6	18, 20, 23	11-1
	5.NF4, 5.NF6	21, 24, 27	11-2
	4.NF4, 5.NF6	22, 26, 29	12-1
	5.NF6	25, 28, 30	12-4
6C	4.NBT5, 5.NBT5	1, 4, 10	3-4
	5.NBT6	2, 5, 7	5-4
	4.NBT5, 5.NBT5	3, 6, 8	3-5
	4.NF6, 5.NBT1, 5.NBT3	9, 11, 14	6-1
	4.NF7, 5.NBT3	12, 13, 16	6-2
	5.NBT7	15, 17, 21	7-1
	4.NF6	18, 20, 28	9-5
	5.NBT7	19, 24, 29	7-2
	5.NBT7	22, 25, 30	8-3
	4.NF2	23, 26, 27	9-3
6D	5.NBT7	1, 9, 21	8-2
	4.NF1	2, 10, 30	9-1
	4.NF6, 5.NBT1, 5.NBT3	3, 15, 19	6-1
	5.G1, 5.G2	4, 13, 23	22-1
	4.NF6	5, 12, 26	9-5
	4.NBT6	6, 11, 27	4-4
	4.NF1	7, 17, 28	9-2
	3.OA5	8, 16, 24	2-4
	5.NBT7, 7.EE3	14, 20, 22	8-4
	5.NBT7	18, 25, 29	8-3

	CCSS Standard	Readiness Assessment Question Number	Assigned Intervention Lesson
6E	4.NBT5	1, 2, 3	3-2
	4.NBT5, 5.NBT5	4, 5, 6	3-5
	5.NBT7	7, 29, 30	8-2
	5.NF4, 5.NF6	8, 9, 10	11-2
	5.NF6	11, 12, 13	12-4
	4.G2, 5.G3, 5.G4	14, 15, 16	19-1
	4.G2, 5.G3, 5.G4	17, 18, 19	19-2
	4.MD3	20, 21, 22	20-1
	4.MD3	23, 24, 25	20-2
	5.MD3, 5.MD4, 5.MD5	26, 27, 28	20-5
6F	4.NBT2	1, 2, 3	1-2
	4.NBT6	4, 5, 6	4-4
	4.NBT6	7, 8, 9	4-5
	5.NBT6	10, 11, 12	5-3
	5.NBT6	13, 14, 15	5-4
	4.NF6, 5.NBT1, 5.NBT3	16, 17, 18	6-1
	4.NF7, 5.NBT3	19, 20, 21	6-2
	5.NBT7	22, 23, 24	7-1
	5.NBT7	25, 26, 27	7-2
	5.NBT7	28, 29, 30	8-3

Readiness Assessment Grade 7

	CCSS Standard	Readiness Assessment Question Number	Assigned Intervention Lesson
7A	5.NF4, 5.NF6	1, 5, 7	11-2
	6.RP1	2, 4, 8	13-1
	6.RP3	3, 9, 11	13-2
	6.RP2, 6.RP3b	6, 10, 13	14-1
	6.RP3	12, 14, 16	14-2
	6.RP3	15, 17, 19	14-3
	6.RP3	18, 20, 22	15-1
	6.RP3c	21, 25, 30	16-1
	5.NBT7, 6.NS3	23, 27, 29	8-5
	6.RP3	24, 26, 28	17-1
7B	5.NBT7	1, 4, 7	8-2
	5.NBT7	2, 5, 8	8-3
	5.NF3	3, 6, 10	9-4
	5.NF1, 5.NF2	9, 11, 13	10-3
	5.NF1, 5.NF2	12, 14, 16	10-4
	6.NS1	15, 17, 18	11-5
	4.NF4, 5.NF6	19, 22, 30	12-1
	4.NF3, 5.NF1	20, 23, 26	12-2
	4.NF3, 5.NF1	21, 24, 28	12-3
	6.NS5, 6.NS6, 6.NS7	25, 27, 29	21-1
7C	3.OA5	1, 12, 14	2-1
	3.OA5, 3.MD7	2, 4, 9	2-2
	5.OA1, 6.EE2c	3, 5, 7	23-1
	6.EE2, 6.EE6	6, 8, 10	23-2
	6.EE3, 6.EE4	11, 13, 16	24-2
	6.EE3	15, 17, 19	24-3
	6.EE7	18, 20, 22	25-1
	6.EE5	21, 23, 25	25-2
	6.EE7	24, 26, 28	25-3
	6.EE7	27, 29, 30	25-4

	CCSS Standard	Readiness Assessment Question Number	Assigned Intervention Lesson
7D	5.NBT7	1, 2, 3	8-2
	4.G2, 5.G3, 5.G4	4, 5, 6	19-1
	4.G2, 5.G3, 5.G4	7, 8, 9	19-2
	4.MD3	10, 11, 12	20-2
	6.G1	13, 14, 15	20-3
	6.G3	16, 17, 18	20-4
	5.MD3, 5.MD4, 5.MD5	19, 20, 21	20-5
	6.EE2	22, 23, 24	23-4
	6.EE5	25, 26, 27	25-2
	6.EE7	28, 29, 30	25-3
7E	4.NBT2	1, 2, 3	1-2
	5.NBT6	4, 5, 6	5-4
	4.NF7, 5.NBT3	7, 8, 9	6-2
	5.NBT7	10, 11, 12	8-3
	4.NF2	13, 14, 15	9-3
	6.RP3c	16, 17, 18	16-2
	6.RP3	19, 20, 21	17-1
	6.RP3	22, 23, 24	17-2
	6.RP3c	25, 26, 27	16-1
	6.RP3	28, 29, 30	17-3
7F	5.NBT7	1, 29, 30	8-2
	4.NF1	2, 3, 4	9-1
	4.NF1	5, 6, 7	9-2
	4.NF2	8, 9, 10	9-3
	4.NF6	11, 12, 13	9-5
	4.NF4, 5.NF4, 5.NF6	14, 15, 16	11-1
	6.RP1	17, 18, 19	13-1
	6.RP3c	20, 21, 22	16-1
	6.RP3c	23, 24, 25	16-2
	6.RP3	26, 27, 28	17-1

Readiness Assessment Grade 8

	CCSS Standard	Readiness Assessment Question Number	Assigned Intervention Lesson
8A	4.NF2	1, 2, 3	9-3
	6.NS5, 6.NS6, 6.NS7	4, 5, 7	21-1
	6.NS7	6, 8, 9	21-2
	6.NS6	10, 11, 15	22-4
	6.NS7	12, 13, 14	22-5
8B	6.NS1, 7.NS3	1, 2, 3	12-5
	6.EE1, 5.NBT2	4, 5, 6	18-1
	5.NBT2	7, 8, 9	18-2
	7.NS1	10, 11, 12	21-3
	7.NS1	13, 14, 15	21-4
	7.NS2	16, 17, 18	21-5
	6.EE3	19, 20, 21	24-3
	6.EE5	22, 23, 24	25-2
	6.EE7	25, 26, 27	25-5
	6.EE7	28, 29, 30	25-6

	CCSS Standard	Readiness Assessment Question Number	Assigned Intervention Lesson
8C	6.RP2, 6.RP3b	1, 6, 12	14-1
	6.RP3	2, 4, 8	15-1
	7.RP2	3, 5, 7	15-2
	7.RP3	9, 10, 13	17-4
	6.NS6	11, 14, 16	22-2
	6.EE3	15, 17, 19	24-3
	6.EE5	18, 20, 22	25-2
	6.EE7	21, 23, 25	25-5
	6.EE7	24, 26, 28	25-6
	7.EE4	27, 29, 30	25-7
8D	6.RP3	1, 6, 11	13-2
	6.RP2, 6.RP3b	2, 4, 12	14-1
	6.RP3	3, 5, 7	15-1
	5.G1, 5.G2	8, 10, 13	22-1
	6.NS6	9, 14, 16	22-2
	6.EE2, 6.EE6	15, 17, 18	23-2
	6.EE2, 6.EE6	19, 21, 30	23-3
	6.EE2	20, 22, 24	23-4
	6.EE2	23, 25, 27	24-1
	6.EE7	26, 28, 29	25-1
8E	5.NBT7	1, 2, 3	8-2
	7.RP2	4, 5, 6	15-2
	7.RP2	7, 8, 9	15-3
	6.EE1, 5.NBT2	10, 11, 12	18-1
	6.G4	13, 14, 15	20-4
	5.MD3, 5.MD4, 5.MD5	16, 17, 18	20-5
	6.NS6	19, 20, 21	22-2
	6.G3	22, 23, 24	22-3
	6.EE2	25, 26, 27	23-4
	6.EE2	28, 29, 30	24-1
8F	4.NF6	1, 2, 3	9-5
	6.RP1	4, 5, 6	13-1
	6.RP3	7, 8, 9	13-2
	6.RP3	10, 11, 12	15-1
	6.RP3c	13, 14, 15	16-1
	6.RP3	16, 17, 18	17-1
	6.RP3	19, 20, 21	17-2
	5.G1, 5.G2	22, 23, 24	22-1
	6.NS6	25, 26, 27	22-2
	6.EE2, 6.EE6	28, 29, 30	23-3

"[digits] integrates lesson planning, homework management, intervention, and assessment, all within a **user-friendly design** that encourages class collaboration via interactive whiteboards."

- MaryAnn Karre,
Tech & Learning Magazine

Instructional Framework

interACTIVE Learning

Supported with Understanding by Design principles, all on-level lessons facilitate interACTIVE Instruction. Students engage with the mathematics through exploration, learn concepts explicitly to formalize the knowledge, and connect newly acquired knowledge to prior knowledge. Multimedia elements provide engaging visual, audio, and kinesthetic support to reach all learners.

Differentiation and individualized intervention is integrated in *digits* through the interACTIVE Learning Cycle™. All instruction focuses on helping students achieve success with on-level content the first time they see it. Unlike other intervention systems, the *digits* system is preventative. Instead of providing remediation after students fail on-level content, intervention in *digits* provides support for necessary prerequisites in advance. By addressing weaknesses up front, students are better prepared to succeed with on-level work. Additionally, unit-based Readiness Assessments enable targeted intervention determined by up-to-date performance data so that students receive exactly the support they need. All differentiation and intervention in *digits* is coherent with and supportive of core on-level instruction.

interACTIVE Instruction

Elements of Understanding by Design

Every on-level lesson has a Focus Question that directs students towards deeper mathematical understanding. The Focus Question helps students think about how various math concepts are interconnected and how they are relevant to students' lives. **Hosts** introduce the Focus Question and appear throughout the lesson to give students additional information about why the specific mathematical concept is important as well as make explicit mathematical relationships.

Each on-level lesson has three parts: Launch, Examples, and Close and Check. The Launch introduces the Focus Question and incorporates problem-based interactive learning to encourage connections to prior knowledge; the Close and Check provides students with an opportunity to answer the Focus Question, complete more practice problems, and record their mathematical thinking. Both parts of the lesson are supported with companion pages for students to record their reasoning and work.

digits Hosts ▼

Fostering Understanding
Monograph by Grant Wiggins

It should seem obvious that the point of instruction in mathematics is **understanding** as reflected in effective problem-solving. Alas, too often mathematics instruction is focused on topic coverage and "plug and chug" work rather than genuine student connections and transfer of learning. Students too often spend valuable instructional time completing computational exercises with a goal of procedural fluency and sparse attention on developing deeper conceptual understanding or strategic competence that would help them become effective and efficient problem-solvers.

The recently released Common Core State Standards for Mathematics (CCSSM) have articulated the goal of **deep mathematical understanding**. This goal is made clear in at least two ways: the focus of understanding is stressed in the Introduction; and curriculum, instruction, and assessment are expected to mesh the Standards for Mathematical Practice with the Standards for Mathematical Content. "Those content standards, which set an expectation of understanding are potential "points of intersection" between the Standards for Mathematical Content and the Standards for Mathematical Practice." (CCSSM, 2010, p. 8)

Understanding by Design is built on this purpose, and thus can provide a useful strategy and set of tools for honoring the spirit and letter of the Common Core State Standards for Mathematics. What's the key? The authors of the CCSSM astutely clarify the aim by focusing on the **assessment** implications (just as we demand in Understanding by Design):

> *Asking a student to understand something means asking a teacher to assess whether the student has understood it. . . One hallmark of mathematical understanding is the ability to justify, in a way appropriate to the student's mathematical maturity, why a particular mathematical statement is true or where a mathematical rule comes from. (CCSSM, 2010, p. 4)*

A steady dose of only simple lessons and questions results in students who "rely on procedures too heavily." With only inflexible recall of skill at their disposal, students are "less likely to consider analogous problems, represent problems coherently, justify conclusions, apply the mathematics to practical situations, use technology mindfully to work with the mathematics, explain the mathematics accurately to other students, step back for an overview, or deviate from a known procedure to find a shortcut." (CCSSM, 2010, p. 8)

Know-how is necessary but insufficient. Real understanding and problem-solving requires knowing why. Only then can you adapt prior learning—transfer your learning—to future problems. Students who understand can apply their learning flexibly and creatively; they are good at using content, not just recalling math facts.

Pearson's *digits* focuses on helping students develop **deep conceptual understanding** of the mathematics they encounter and **strong problem-solving and reasoning abilities**, with the goal of ensuring that students understand and are able to do mathematics. When students are grounded in conceptual understanding, problem-solving, and reasoning, students can achieve true mathematical proficiency.

Launch

In *digits*, students engage with mathematical content at the start of class through Problem-Based Interactive Learning. Students work on a real-world problem that enables them to make use of and build on prior knowledge in order to construct new knowledge.

The **Launch** is supported with a **Companion page** and content for the interactive whiteboard or projector screen. Teachers can invite students to the interactive whiteboard to share their solutions and strategies, including using the interactive whiteboard tools or manipulating objects on the screen.

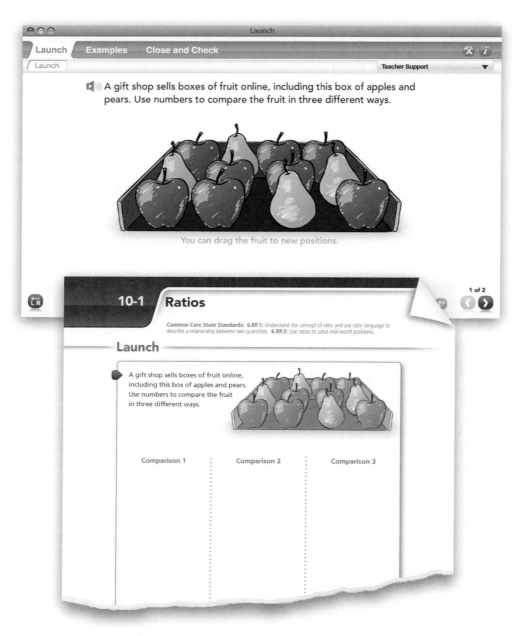

After students complete the Launch problem, they are asked the **Focus Question** which they are to consider as they move through each Example. The Focus Question is introduced by a host. The hosts are real, young, successful students who middle-graders can look up to. This allows young learners to engage with the math on a new, relatable level. The hosts guide students through the lesson by providing context and reasons for why learning the concept is important, and they do this sincerely and authentically, in their own words.

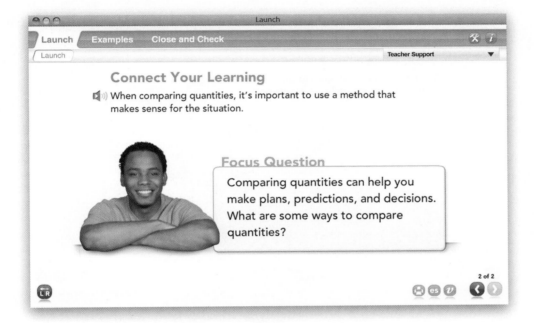

Examples

The examples in *digits* provide direct, explicit instruction of the lesson's concept. The examples build on one another to ensure understanding.

Various **animations** are built in to support comprehension and engagement. Visual elements such as color-coding, pulsing, and movement draw students' attention to the important details of the concept.

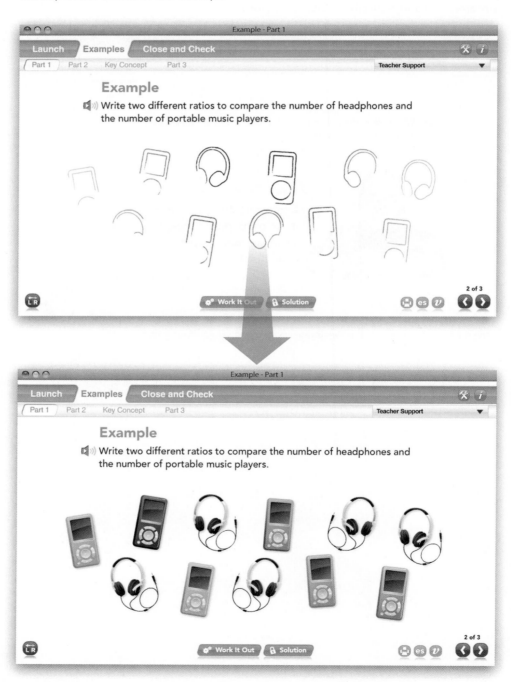

Every example concludes with **formative assessment** to check for understanding. Student performance on the assessment item can be used to make immediate instructional decisions, such as modifying the pace or reviewing a concept to prevent the development of deeper misconceptions. Each formative assessment item following each example can be delivered in a variety of formats.

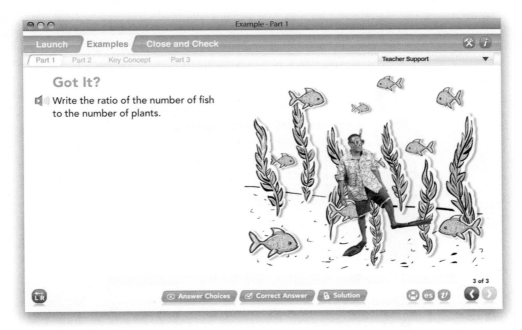

The **Key Concept** summarizes the content of the lesson to support understanding.

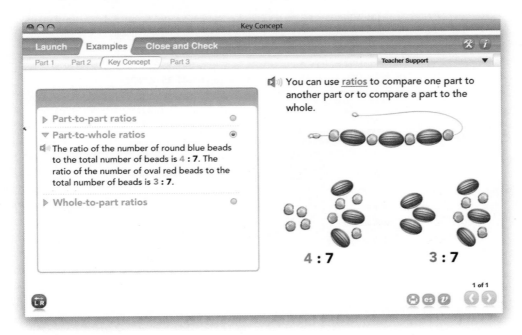

Close and Check

The Close and Check brings students back to the **Focus Question**, which they now answer in their write-in student companion. The Focus Question is designed to enable students to think about the Launch problem and Examples coherently. Additionally, students complete **practice problems** that are similar to the Examples and answer higher-order questions that require interpretation and analysis.

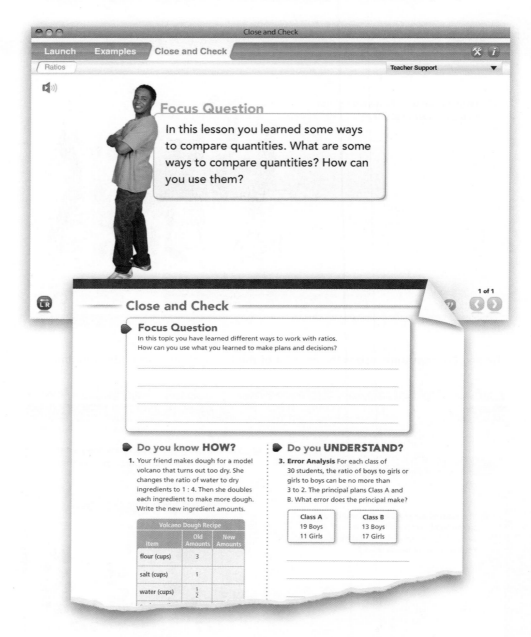

Close and Check

Launch   Examples   **Close and Check**

Ratios   Teacher Support

Focus Question

In this lesson you learned some ways to compare quantities. What are some ways to compare quantities? How can you use them?

1 of 1

Close and Check

Focus Question

In this topic you have learned different ways to work with ratios. How can you use what you learned to make plans and decisions?

_____

_____

_____

_____

Do you know **HOW?**

1. Your friend makes dough for a model volcano that turns out too dry. She changes the ratio of water to dry ingredients to 1 : 4. Then she doubles each ingredient to make more dough. Write the new ingredient amounts.

Volcano Dough Recipe		
Item	Old Amounts	New Amounts
flour (cups)	3	
salt (cups)	1	
water (cups)	$\frac{1}{2}$	

Do you **UNDERSTAND?**

3. **Error Analysis** For each class of 30 students, the ratio of boys to girls or girls to boys can be no more than 3 to 2. The principal plans Class A and B. What error does the principal make?

Class A
19 Boys
11 Girls

Class B
13 Boys
17 Girls

_____

_____

Topic Review

In the Topic Review, students work on **Pull It All Together**, a rich performance task that provides an authentic problem-solving experience.

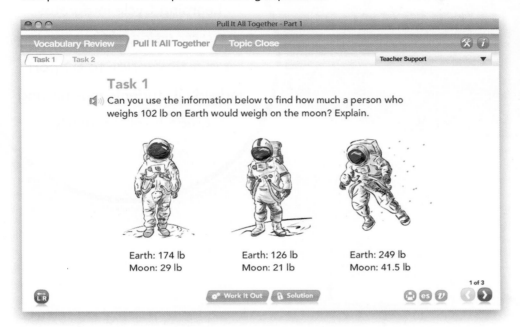

At the end of each Topic, students revisit the **Essential Question** for the Topic. This activity is a summary point in Understanding by Design principles—students answer the larger questions of when, how, and why to use the skills and concepts they have learned in the Topic.

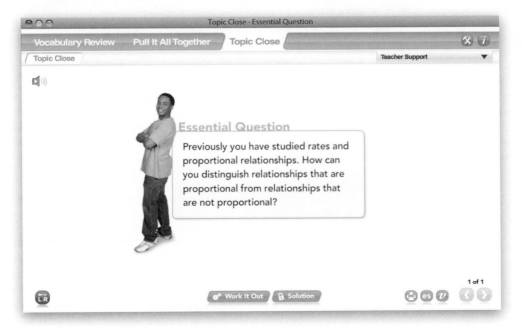

interACTIVE Learning Cycle

The interACTIVE Learning Cycle integrates *core instruction*, *differentiation*, and *intervention* to support individual students in achieving grade-level standards.

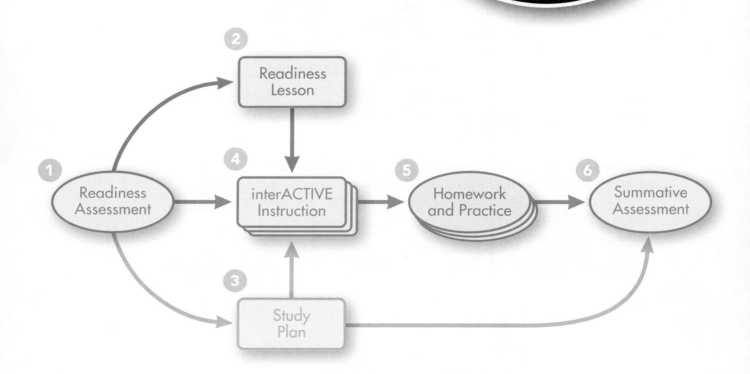

● **Blue** - whole class   ● **Purple** - differentiated   ● Orange - individualized

Readiness Assessment

The Readiness Assessment screens every student on their understanding of the pre-requisite content of the unit.

Readiness Lesson

The Readiness Lesson incorporates small group work driven by the data of the Readiness Assessment. Students who are deficient in the pre-requisites are provided with additional instruction while other students work on extending their understanding.

Personalized Study Plans

Personalized Study Plans are generated from the results of the Readiness Assessment. Each student receives a study plan with additional instruction and practice tailored to their specific areas of deficiency.

interACTIVE Instruction

Core on-level instruction is interactive with visual learning supports and multimedia to engage students. Formative assessment is integrated to inform pacing and other instruction decisions during class.

Differentiated Homework/Practice

On-level instruction is supported with homework and practice differentiated according to the results of the Readiness Assessment.

Summative Assessment

Summative Assessments at the end of a topic and at the end of a unit provide on-going progress monitoring of students' comprehension of instruction.

Enrichment Projects

Teachers can elect to assign enrichment projects to students who demonstrate no or little deficiencies in prerequisites. Projects span the entire unit and focus on higher-order thinking.

Response to Intervention

digits applies both prevention and remediation in its unique approach to intervention. By addressing prerequisite deficiencies prior to grade-level content instruction, students are more likely to be successful with new material the first time around. Ongoing progress monitoring synchronized with adaptive intervention instruction serves students precisely at point of need and clarifies misconceptions and areas of confusion before they accumulate.

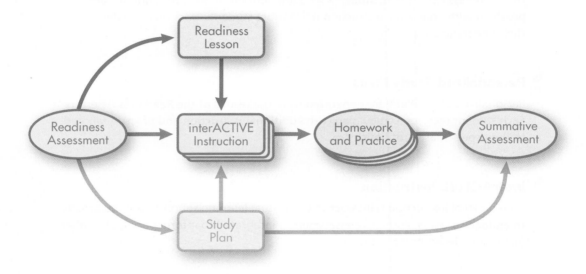

● **Blue** - whole class   ● **Purple** - differentiated   ● **Orange** - individualized

Tier 1: Core Instruction

Recommendation	in *digits*
Universal screener assesses students and identifies areas of weakness	Readiness Assessments for each unit screen students regularly
Universal design principles address the needs of specialized populations while benefiting all	• Visual and kinesthetic learning engage students • Explicit cognitive guidance for solving problems, structured problems, and prompts aid comprehension
Ongoing progress monitoring gauges students' response to instruction	• Topic and Unit Assessments monitor student progress on content acquisition • Benchmark Assessments monitor student progress against grade-level expectations

Tier 2: Prevention

Recommendation	in *digits*
Prerequisite deficiencies are identified and addressed within the classroom routine prior to new content instruction	Readiness Lessons provide pre-requisite instruction for students with deficiencies and extension for students without deficiencies
Prevention activities are not disruptive to the target children and nonintrusive to classmates	• Small group activities support Team-Assisted Instruction • Differentiated practice and homework with student triggered learning aids meet cognitive needs appropriately

Tier 3: Strategic Intervention

Recommendation	in *digits*
Strategic intervention enables success with grade-level content	Data-driven individualized Study Plans provide intensive instruction for specific areas of weakness as it relates to grade-level content
Strategic intervention is individualized or provided in small groups	Digital lessons support independent study, one-on-one tutoring, or small group instruction

Program Structure

The interACTIVE Learning Cycle provides a simplified view of the program's instructional pathway with data-driven branching for differentiation and personalization at the unit level.

Units in *digits* are subdivided into topics. Each topic includes a Readiness Lesson, approximately six to ten on-level lessons, a Topic Review, and a Topic Test. Topic resources represented in the interACTIVE Learning Cycle are circled and expanded below.

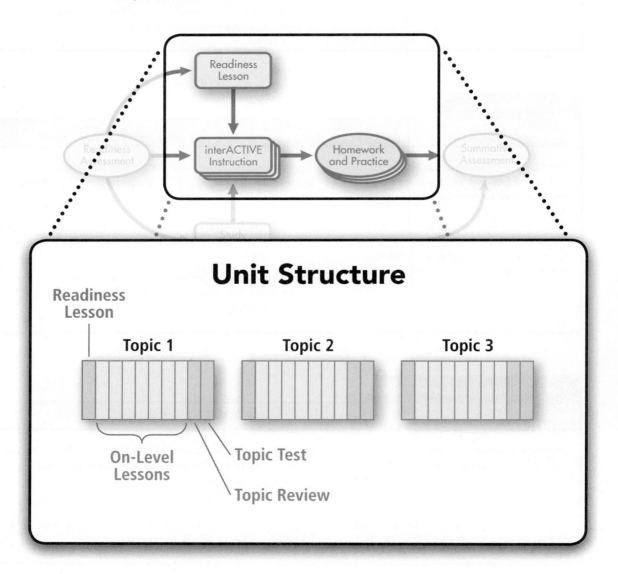

Grade 6 Table of Contents

Grade 7 Table of Contents

Grade 8 Table of Contents

Grade 6
Block Scheduling Pacing Guide

UNIT A

Topic 1: Variables and Expressions

DAY 1		DAY 2		DAY 3		DAY 4		DAY 5	
Readiness Assessment for Unit A	Readiness Lesson for Topic 1	Numerical Expressions	Algebraic Expressions	Writing Algebraic Expressions	Evaluating Algebraic Expressions	Expressions With Exponents	Problem Solving	Topic Review	Readiness Lesson for Topic 2

Topic 2: Equivalent Expressions

DAY 6		DAY 7		DAY 8		DAY 9		DAY 10	
Topic Assessment	The Identity and Zero Properties	The Commutative Properties	The Associative Properties	Greatest Common Factor	The Distributive Property	Least Common Multiple	Problem Solving	Topic Review	Readiness Lesson for Topic 3

Topic 3: Equations and Inequalities

DAY 11		DAY 12		DAY 13		DAY 14		DAY 15	
Topic Assessment	Expressions to Equations	Balancing Equations	Solving Addition and Subtraction Equations	Solving Multiplication and Division Equations	Equations to Inequalities	Solving Inequalities	Problem Solving	Topic Review	Readiness Assessment for Unit B

Topic 4: Two-Variable Relationships

DAY 16		DAY 17		DAY 18		DAY 19		DAY 20	
Topic Assessment	Readiness Lesson for Topic 4	Using Two Variables to Represent a Relationship	Analyzing Patterns Using Tables and Graphs	Relating Tables and Graphs to Equations	Problem Solving	Topic Review	Readiness Lesson for Topic 5	Topic Assessment	Unit Assessment

UNIT B

Topic 5: Multiplying Fractions | Topic 6

DAY 21		DAY 22		DAY 23		DAY 24		DAY 25	
Multiplying Fractions and Whole Numbers	Multiplying Two Fractions	Multiplying Fractions and Mixed Numbers	Multiplying Mixed Numbers	Problem Solving	Topic Review	Topic Assessment	Readiness Assessment for Unit C	Readiness Lesson for Topic 6	Dividing Fractions and Whole Numbers

Topic 6: Dividing Fractions

DAY 26		DAY 27		DAY 28		DAY 29		DAY 30	
Dividing Unit Fractions by Unit Fractions	Dividing Fractions and Whole Numbers	Dividing Mixed Numbers	Problem Solving	Topic Review	Readiness Lesson for Topic 7	Topic Assessment	Unit Assessment	Adding and Subtracting Decimals	Multiplying Decimals

UNIT C

Topic 7

Topic 7: Fluency with Decimals

DAY 31		DAY 32		DAY 33		DAY 34		DAY 35	
Dividing Multi-Digit Numbers	Dividing Decimals	Decimals and Fractions	Comparing and Ordering Decimals and Fractions	Problem Solving	Topic Review	Topic Assessment	Readiness Lesson for Topic 8	Integers and the Number Line	Comparing and Ordering Integers

Topic 8: Integers

Topic 9: Rational Numbers

DAY 36		DAY 37		DAY 38		DAY 39		DAY 40	
Absolute Value	Integers and the Coordinate Plane	Distance	Problem Solving	Topic Review	Readiness Assessment for Unit D	Topic Assessment	Readiness Lesson for Topic 9	Rational Numbers and the Number Line	Comparing Rational Numbers

UNIT D

Topic 10: Ratios

DAY 41		DAY 42		DAY 43		DAY 44		DAY 45	
Ordering Rational Numbers	Rational Numbers and the Coordinate Plane	Polygons in the Coordinate Plane	Problem Solving	Topic Review	Readiness Lesson for Topic 10	Topic Assessment	Unit Assessment	Ratios	Exploring Equivalent Ratios

Topic 11: Rates

DAY 46		DAY 47		DAY 48		DAY 49		DAY 50	
Equivalent Ratios	Ratios as Fractions	Ratios as Decimals	Problem Solving	Topic Review	Readiness Lesson for Topic 11	Topic Assessment	Unit Rates	Unit Prices	Constant Speed

Topic 12: Ratio Reasoning

DAY 51		DAY 52		DAY 53		DAY 54		DAY 55	
Measurement and Ratios	Choosing the Appropriate Rate	Problem Solving	Topic Review	Topic Assessment	Readiness Assessment for Unit E	Readiness Lesson for Topic 12	Plotting Ratios and Rates	Recognizing Proportionality	Introducing Percents

UNIT E

Topic 13: Area

DAY 56		DAY 57		DAY 58		DAY 59		DAY 60	
Using Percents	Problem Solving	Topic Review	Readiness Lesson for Topic 13	Topic Assessment	Unit Assessment	Rectangles and Squares	Right Triangles	Parallelograms	Other Triangles

Topic 14: Surface Area and Volume

DAY 61		DAY 62		DAY 63		DAY 64		DAY 65	
Polygons	Problem Solving	Topic Review	Readiness Assessment for Unit F	Topic Assessment	Readiness Lesson for Topic 14	Analyzing Three-Dimensional Figures	Nets	Surface Areas of Prisms	Surface Areas of Pyramids

UNIT F

Topic 15: Data Displays

DAY 66		DAY 67		DAY 68		DAY 69		DAY 70	
Volumes of Rectangular Prisms	Problem Solving	Topic Review	Readiness Lesson for Topic 15	Topic Assessment	Unit Assessment	Statistical Questions	Dot Plots	Histograms	Box Plots

Topic 16: Measures of Center and Variation

DAY 71		DAY 72		DAY 73		DAY 74		DAY 75	
Choosing an Appropriate Display	Problem Solving	Topic Review	Readiness Lesson for Topic 16	Topic Assessment	Median	Mean	Variability	Interquartile Range	Mean Absolute Deviation

DAY 76		DAY 77	
Problem Solving	Topic Review	Topic Assessment	Unit Assessment

Grade 7
Block Scheduling Pacing Guide

UNIT A

Topic 1: Ratios and Rates | Topic 2

DAY 1		DAY 2		DAY 3		DAY 4		DAY 5	
Readiness Assessment for Unit A	Readiness Lesson for Topic 1	Equivalent Ratios	Unit Rates	Ratios With Fractions	Unit Rates With Fractions	Problem Solving	Topic Review	Topic Assessment	Readiness Lesson for Topic 2

Topic 2: Proportional Relationships | Topic 3

DAY 6		DAY 7		DAY 8		DAY 9		DAY 10	
Proportional Relationships and Tables	Proportional Relationships and Graphs	Constant of Proportionality	Proportional Relationships and Equations	Maps and Scale Drawings	Problem Solving	Topic Review	Readiness Assessment for Unit B	Topic Assessment	Readiness Lesson for Topic 3

Topic 3: Percents

DAY 11		DAY 12		DAY 13		DAY 14		DAY 15	
The Percent Equation	Using the Percent Equation	Simple Interest	Compound Interest	Percent Increase and Decrease	Markups and Markdowns	Problem Solving	Topic Review	Topic Assessment	Unit Assessment

UNIT B

Topic 4: Adding and Subtracting Rational Numbers

DAY 16		DAY 17		DAY 18		DAY 19		DAY 20	
Readiness Lesson for Topic 4	Rational Numbers, Opposites, and Absolute Value, and Opposite	Adding Integers	Adding Rational Numbers	Subtracting Integers	Subtracting Rational Numbers	Distance on a Number Line	Problem Solving	Topic Review	Readiness Lesson for Topic 5

Topic 5: Multiplying and Dividing Rational Numbers

DAY 21		DAY 22		DAY 23		DAY 24		DAY 25	
Topic Assessment	Multiplying Integers	Multiplying Rational Numbers	Dividing Integers	Dividing Rational Numbers	Operations with Rational Numbers	Problem Solving	Topic Review	Topic Assessment	Readiness Assessment for Unit C

Topic 6: Decimals and Percent

DAY 26		DAY 27		DAY 28		DAY 29		DAY 30	
Readiness Lesson for Topic 6	Repeating Decimals	Terminating Decimals	Percents Greater Than 100	Percents Less Than 1	Fractions, Decimals, and Percents	Percent Error	Problem Solving	**Topic Review**	**Readiness Lesson for Topic 7**

UNIT C

Topic 7: Equivalent Expressions | Topic 8

DAY 31		DAY 32		DAY 33		DAY 34		DAY 35	
Topic Assessment	**Unit Assessment**	Expanding Algebraic Expressions	Factoring Algebraic Expressions	Adding Algebraic Expressions	Subtracting Algebraic Expressions	Problem Solving	**Topic Review**	**Topic Assessment**	**Readiness Lesson for Topic 8**

Topic 8: Equations | Topic 9

DAY 36		DAY 37		DAY 38		DAY 39		DAY 40	
Solving Simple Equations	Writing Two-Step Equations	Solving Two-Step Equations	Solving Equations Using the Distributive Property	Problem Solving	**Topic Review**	**Topic Assessment**	**Readiness Assessment for Unit D**	**Readiness Lesson for Topic 9**	Solving Inequalities Using Addition or Subtraction

UNIT D

Topic 9: Inequalities | Topic 10

DAY 41		DAY 42		DAY 43		DAY 44		DAY 45	
Solving Inequalities Using Multiplication or Division	Solving Two-Step Inequalities	Solving Multi-Step Inequalities	Problem Solving	**Topic Review**	**Readiness Lesson for Topic 10**	**Topic Assessment**	**Unit Assessment**	Measuring Angles	Adjacent Angles

Topic 10: Angles | Topic 11: Circles

DAY 46		DAY 47		DAY 48		DAY 49		DAY 50	
Complementary Angles	Supplementary Angles	Vertical Angles	Problem Solving	**Topic Review**	**Readiness Lesson for Topic 11**	**Topic Assessment**	Center, Radius, and Diameter	Circumference of a Circle	Area of a Circle

Topic 12: 2- and 3-Dimensional Shapes

DAY 51		DAY 52		DAY 53		DAY 54		DAY 55	
Relating Circumference and Area of a Circle	Problem Solving	**Topic Review**	**Readiness Lesson for Topic 12**	**Topic Assessment**	Geometry Drawing Tools	Drawing Triangles with Given Conditions 1	Drawing Triangles with Given Conditions 2	2-D Slices of Rectangular Prisms	2-D Slices of Right Rectangular Pyramids

Topic 13: Surface Area and Volume

DAY 56		DAY 57		DAY 58		DAY 59		DAY 60	
Problem Solving	Topic Review	Topic Assessment	Readiness Assessment for Unit E	Readiness Lesson for Topic 13	Surface Areas of Right Prisms	Volumes of Right Prisms	Surface Areas of Right Pyramids	Volumes of Right Pyramids	Problem Solving

UNIT E

Topic 14: Sampling

DAY 61		DAY 62		DAY 63		DAY 64		DAY 65	
Topic Review	Readiness Lesson for Topic 14	Topic Assessment	Unit Assessment	Populations and Samples	Estimating a Population	Convenience Sampling	Systematic Sampling	Simple Random Sampling	Comparing Sampling Methods

Topic 15: Comparing Two Populations

DAY 66		DAY 67		DAY 68		DAY 69		DAY 70	
Problem Solving	Topic Review	Topic Assessment	Readiness Assessment for Unit F	Readiness Lesson for Topic 15	Statistical Measures	Multiple Populations and Inferences	Using Measures of Center	Using Measures of Variability	Exploring Overlap in Data Sets

UNIT F

Topic 16: Probability Concepts

DAY 71		DAY 72		DAY 73		DAY 74		DAY 75	
Problem Solving	Topic Review	Topic Assessment	Unit Assessment	Readiness Lesson for Topic 16	Likelihood and Probability	Sample Space	Relative Frequency and Experimental Probability	Theoretical Probability	Probability Models

Topic 17: Compound Events

DAY 76		DAY 77		DAY 78		DAY 79		DAY 80	
Problem Solving	Topic Review	Topic Assessment	Readiness Lesson for Topic 17	Compound Events	Sample Spaces of Compound Events	Finding Compound Probabilities Using Organizational Lists	Finding Compound Probabilities Using Tables	Finding Compound Probabilities Using Tree Diagrams	Simulating Compound Events

DAY 81		DAY 82	
Problem Solving	Topic Review	Topic Assessment	Unit Assessment

Grade 8
Block Scheduling Pacing Guide

UNIT A

Topic 1: Rational and Irrational Numbers

DAY 1		DAY 2		DAY 3		DAY 4		DAY 5	
Readiness Assessment for Unit A	Readiness Lesson for Topic 1	Expressing Rational Numbers with Decimal Exp's.	Exploring Irrational Numbers	Approximating Irrational Numbers	Comparing and Ordering Rational and Irrational #s	Problem Solving	Topic Review	Topic Assessment	Readiness Assessment for Unit B

UNIT B

Topic 2: Linear Equations in One Variable   Topic 3

DAY 6		DAY 7		DAY 8		DAY 9		DAY 10	
Unit Assessment	Readiness Lesson for Topic 2	Solving Two-Step Equations	Solving Equations with Variables on Both Sides	Solving Equations Using the Distributive Property	Solutions – One, None, or Infinitely Many	Problem Solving	Topic Review	Topic Assessment	Readiness Lesson for Topic 3

Topic 3: Integer Exponents

DAY 11		DAY 12		DAY 13		DAY 14		DAY 15	
Perfect Squares, Square Roots, and Equations of the form $x^2 = p$	Perfect Cubes, Cube Roots, and Equations of the form $x^3 = p$	Exponents and Multiplication	Exponents and Division	Zero and Negative Exponents	Comparing Expressions with Exponents	Problem Solving	Topic Review	Topic Assessment	Readiness Assessment for Unit C

Topic 4: Scientific Notation

DAY 16		DAY 17		DAY 18		DAY 19		DAY 20	
Readiness Lesson for Topic 4	Exploring Scientific Notation	Using Scientific Notation to Describe Very Large Quantities	Using Scientific Notation to Describe Very Small Quantities	Operating with Numbers Expressed in Scientific Notation	Problem Solving	Topic Review	Readiness Lesson for Topic 5	Topic Assessment	Unit Assessment

UNIT C

Topic 5: Proportional Relationships, Lines, and Linear Equations

DAY 21		DAY 22		DAY 23		DAY 24		DAY 25	
Graphing Proportional Relationships	Linear Equations: $y = mx$	The Slope of a Line	Unit Rates and Slope	The y-intercept of a Line	Linear Equations: $y = mx + b$	Problem Solving	Topic Review	Topic Assessment	Readiness Assessment for Unit D

Topic 6: Systems of Two Linear Equations

DAY 26		DAY 27		DAY 28		DAY 29		DAY 30	
Readiness Lesson for Topic 6	What is a System of Linear Equations in Two…	Estimating Solutions of Linear Systems by Inspection	Solving Systems of Linear Equations by Graphing	Solving Systems of Linear Equations Using Substitution	Solving Systems of Linear Equations Using Addition	Solving Systems of Linear Equations Using Subtraction	Problem Solving	Topic Review	Readiness Lesson for Topic 7

UNIT D

Topic 7: Defining and Comparing Functions

DAY 31		DAY 32		DAY 33		DAY 34		DAY 35	
Topic Assessment	Unit Assessment	Recognizing a Function	Representing a Function	Linear Functions	Nonlinear Functions	Increasing and Decreasing Intervals	Sketching a Function Graph	Problem Solving	Topic Review

Topic 8: Linear Functions

DAY 36		DAY 37		DAY 38		DAY 39		DAY 40	
Topic Assessment	Readiness Assessment for Unit E	Readiness Lesson for Topic 8	Defining a Linear Function Rule	Rate of Change	Initial Value	Comparing Two Linear Functions	Constructing a Function to Model a Linear Relationship	Problem Solving	Topic Review

UNIT E

Topic 9: Congruence

DAY 41		DAY 42		DAY 43		DAY 44		DAY 45	
Topic Assessment	Unit Assessment	Readiness Lesson for Topic 9	Translations	Reflections	Rotations	Congruent Figures	Problem Solving	Topic Review	Readiness Lesson for Topic 10

Topic 10: Similarity / Topic 11

DAY 46		DAY 47		DAY 48		DAY 49		DAY 50	
Topic Assessment	Dilations	Similar Figures	Relating Similar Triangles and Slope	Problem Solving	Topic Review	Topic Assessment	Readiness Lesson for Topic 11	Angles, Lines, and Transversals	Reasoning and Parallel Lines

Topic 11: Reasoning in Geometry / Topic 12

DAY 51		DAY 52		DAY 53		DAY 54		DAY 55	
Interior Angles of Triangles	Exterior Angles of Triangles	Angle-Angle Triangle Similarity	Problem Solving	Topic Review	Readiness Lesson for Topic 12	Topic Assessment	Reasoning and Proof	The Pythagorean Theorem	Finding Unknown Leg Lengths

Topic 12: Using the Pythagorean Theorem

DAY 56		DAY 57		DAY 58	
The Converse of the Pythagorean Theorem	Distance in the Coordinate Plane	Problem Solving	Topic Review	Topic Assessment	Readiness Assessment for Unit F

Topic 13: Surface Area and Volume

DAY 59		DAY 60	
Readiness Lesson for Topic 13	Surface Areas of Cylinders	Volumes of Cylinders	Surface Areas of Cones

DAY 61		DAY 62		DAY 63		DAY 64		DAY 65	
Volumes of Cones	Surface Areas of Spheres	Volumes of Spheres	Problem Solving	Topic Review	Readiness Lesson for Topic 14	Topic Assessment	Unit Assessment	Interpreting a Scatter Plot	Constructing a Scatter Plot

Topic 14

UNIT F

Topic 14: Scatter Plots

DAY 66		DAY 67		DAY 68	
Investigating Patterns – Clustering and Outliers	Investigating Patterns - Association	Linear Models – Fitting a Straight Line	Linear Models – Using the Equation of a Linear Model	Problem Solving	Topic Review

Topic 15: Relative Frequency

DAY 69		DAY 70	
Topic Assessment	Readiness Lesson for Topic 15	Bivariate Categorical Data	Constructing Two-Way Frequency Tables

DAY 71		DAY 72		DAY 73		DAY 74	
Interpreting Two-Way Frequency Tables	Constructing Two-Way Relative Frequency Tables	Interpreting Two-Way Relative Frequency Tables	Choosing a Measure of Frequency	Problem Solving	Topic Review	Topic Assessment	Unit Assessment

Progress Monitoring

Homework and Practice

Homework and practice in *digits* is powered by MathXL for School, an award-winning program used by over 5 million students nationwide. Assignments are differentiated according to the results of the Readiness Assessment. Students with prerequisite deficiencies are provided with supportive practice problems that help develop mathematical thinking and students with little or no deficiencies are provided additional challenge to extend their understanding.

Items are presented in a variety of formats including multiple choice, gridded response, and open response. Additionally, they are algorithmically generated, which provides students with unlimited practice.

Help Me Solve This scaffolds the problem by breaking it down into individual steps. Students are provided with instant feedback for each step in order to address any misconceptions at the source.

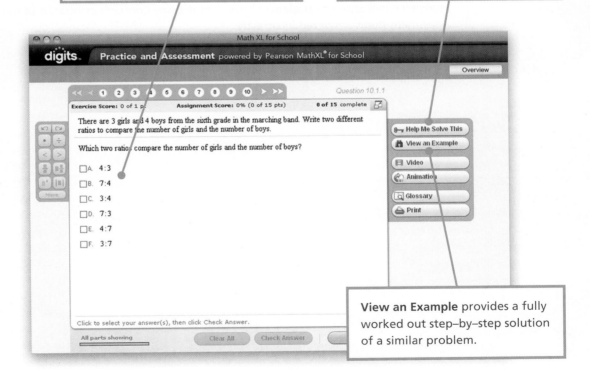

View an Example provides a fully worked out step–by–step solution of a similar problem.

The homework and practice in *digits* provides teachers with daily formative assessment data to drive instruction. Because teachers can view results in their gradebooks immediately, they can adapt instruction for the very next lesson. Paired with the lesson's Close and Check, teachers have both qualitative student data with work shown in the companion and quantitative student data with homework and practice results tabulated in the gradebook.

Assessments

Diagnostic assessments include a Beginning of Year test as well as Readiness Assessments at the start of each unit.

Summative assessments in *digits* are comprehensive.

- ☑ Topic Tests assess a collection of related lessons
- ☑ Unit Tests assess a group of related topics
- ☑ Mid-year Test assesses the first half of the course
- ☑ Full-year Test assess the entire course

Additionally, Topic Tests are available with or without study plans. The Topic Test Study Plan will assign to students a review of the Key Concepts associated to the assessment items answered incorrectly.

Four benchmark assessments are also available to measure students' progress against grade-level standards.

Scoring and Reporting

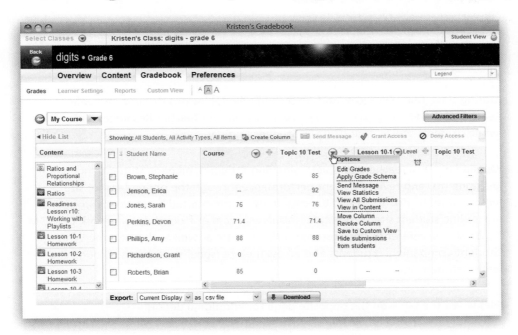

When completed online, all homework, practice, and assessments are automatically graded and tabulated into the gradebook. Any assessments completed offline can be manually entered into the gradebook.

Once in the gradebook, the data can be sorted and filtered according to your needs. A variety of reports are also available such as:

- ☑ Assignment Details Report

- ☑ Mastery by Standard

- ☑ Mastery by Skill

Components

Components in *digits* are streamlined to minimize materials management.

During class, teachers access and present the digital lessons through the online teacher site www.digitsDashboard.com, or from the Teacher Resources DVD-ROM while students utilize their Write-in Student Companions.

Outside of class, teachers complete planning activities, manage student assignments, and review student performance through the online teacher site www.digitsDashboard.com. Students access differentiated homework through the online student site www.MyMathUniverse.com or from the Homework CD-ROM. Students can reference class lessons on the website as well as through the Write-in Student Companion. Students also access their personal study plans through the online student site.

Please see the table on the opposite page for additional details.

Student Package

MyMathUniverse.com

- ☑ class lessons
- ☑ differentiated homework
- ☑ personal study plan
- ☑ automatic software updates
  - *performance improvements*
  - *feature enhancements*
- ☑ digital content updates
  - *state standards revisions*
  - *other revisions or additions*

Write-in Student Companion

- ☑ two worktext pages per on-level lesson
- ☑ annual printed content updates
  - *state standards revisions*
  - *other revisions or additions*

Teacher Package

digitsDashboard.com

- ☑ class lessons
- ☑ lesson planning tools
- ☑ student and assignment management tools
- ☑ assessment and data management tools
- ☑ automatic software updates
  - *performance improvements*
  - *feature enhancements*
- ☑ digital content updates
  - *state standards revisions*
  - *other revisions or additions*

Resource Kit

- ☑ Program Overview Guide
- ☑ Teacher Resources DVD-ROM
  - *class lessons*
  - *lesson plans*
  - *reproducible masters*
  - *answer keys*
- ☑ Student Homework Assignments CD-ROM (five copies)

Teaching

Flexible Design

Lessons in *digits* are designed for flexibility so that teachers can incorporate their own personal styles and best practices. Teachers control what information is displayed to the class as well as when to show it. Simple navigation allows teachers to sequence the lesson presentation as they see most appropriate for their students. On-demand tools enable teachers to explore concepts more deeply and in immediate response to student probes.

Getting Started

digits Dashboard

Be sure to bookmark your ***digits*** dashboard url: **www.digitsDashboard.com**. Your ***digits*** dashboard is your command central—where you can access ***digits*** help and support, view helpful training videos on MyPearsonTraining, and log in to your ***digits*** account. Check back often to view new helpful messages from our authors and links to resources.

1 Log in to ***digits*** using your assigned username and password, or register as a new user.

2 ***digits*** **Overview Videos**
Explore everything that ***digits*** has to offer.

3 **CoCo**
Access all support and resources at ***digits*** Community Connections.

4 **MyPearson Training**
Check out these teacher training videos.

5 ***digits*** **Community**
Reach out to other ***digits*** teachers.

Community Connections (CoCo)

Find support, resources, and links to all things *digits* on our Community Connections page. You can access this page by clicking the CoCo link on your *digits* dashboard, or by clicking the "Take a Tour" button on your teacher home page after you have logged in.

Occasionally, additional resources are posted in a password-protected area of CoCo. Should you need to access this content, use the following username and password.

Username: digitsteacher
Password: digitsmath5

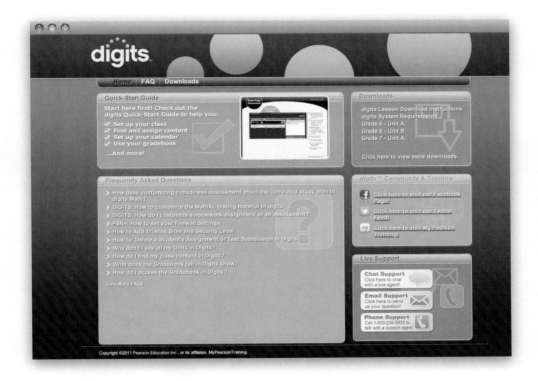

Basics

Lessons in *digits* are designed to promote interactivity with various features and functionality built in for use at your discretion. Although the teacher support materials provide detailed information on how to use each interactive element, the program is intentionally designed to empower teachers to make adjustments that will best serve their students.

Lesson Navigation

The on-level lesson has three major parts: Launch, Examples, and Close and Check. Simple navigation allows you to easily move between these three parts, find a specific example, or a specific screen.

1 **Main Navigation Bar** enables you to move between the major parts of the lesson

2 **Secondary Navigation Bar** provides quick access to each example

3 The **Left-Right button** enables you to move the Screen controls to the left or right side of the screen

4 **Screen controls** allow you to advance each example or lesson part on your command

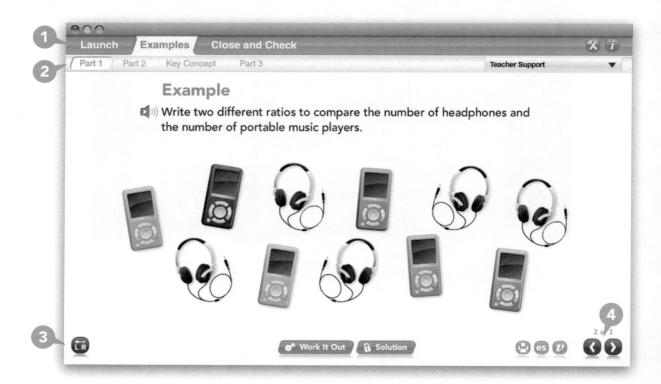

Universal Features

Every page has a set of universal features for access at any time. Universal features include audio support, Math Tools, Standards coverage information, Teaching Support, printing, Spanish translation, and Vocabulary and Key Concepts.

5 Audio Support

6 Print

7 Spanish translation
of the on-screen text

8 Vocabulary and Key Concepts

9 Teaching Support notes and links

10 Math Tools

11 Standards covered in the lesson

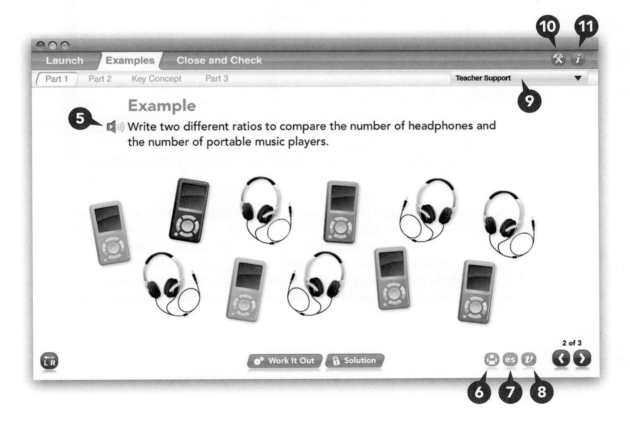

Math Tools

Clicking on the **Math Tools icon** opens a new window with a list of the math tools.

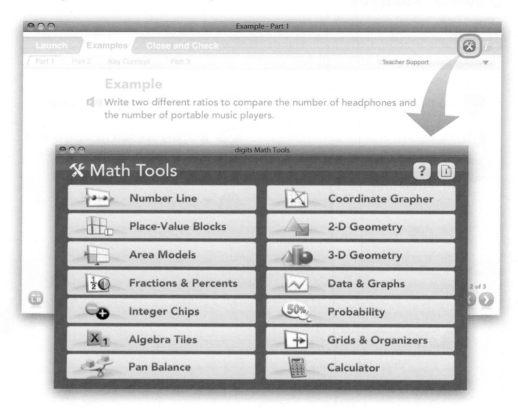

Math Tools for the *digits* program are virtual manipulatives that enable users to interact with, develop, and model math concepts in real time. The tools support teachers in constructing and teaching math concepts visually. The tools also support students in exploring variations of a given math concept and deepening their understanding of the concept. You can open multiple copies of the same tool or a variety of tools at the same time to compare different strategies among students.

Number Line

- Graph integers, decimals, fractions, mixed numbers, and display their opposites and absolute values on a number line.

- Graph single and compound inequalities.

- Model addition and subtraction of fractions, mixed numbers, integers, and decimals.

Place-Value Blocks

- Model and solve base 10 whole number and decimal place-value expressions using place-value blocks.

Area Models

- Explore the multiplication of fractions and mixed numbers, the relationship between squares and square roots, and the relationship between cubes and cube roots using a grid array.

Fractions and Percents

- Model fractions and mixed numbers using strip and pie models.

- Model addition and subtraction of fractions.

- Find a part, whole, or percent in a proportion.

Integer Chips

- Model and solve expressions using integer chips.

Algebra Tiles

- Model and manipulate one-variable algebraic expressions and equations using algebra tiles.

Pan Balance

- Model, compare, and manipulate expressions, equations, and inequalities using natural number values on a pan balance.

Coordinate Grapher

- Construct lines, inequalities, or a system of lines or inequalities.

- Plot and move data points.

- Show trace, line of best fit, and solutions graphically.

2-D Geometry

- Construct and manipulate 2-D geometric figures and shapes to discover their properties and help prove theorems and postulates.

- Measure angles, lengths, and area.

- Explore triangles given specific conditions to determine if they are unique.

3-D Geometry

- Graph 3-D figures such as prisms, pyramids, spheres, cylinders, and cones, and then explore their properties.

- Explore, measure, and compare nets, volumes, and surface areas of 3-D figures.

Data & Graphs

- Add or import data sets into a table, and then select a graph type to display and manipulate the data sets.

Probability

- Perform simulations using real-world objects.

- Compare experimental probability to theoretical probability.

Grids & Organizers

- Select a visual construct to capture students' thoughts and reasoning.

- Apply and support the Standards for Mathematical Practice of the Common Core State Standards.

Calculator

- Displays stacked fractions, percents, squares and square roots, cubes and cube roots, exponents with any base, and expressions within parentheses.

- Generate and display a ten-digit random decimal between 0 and 1, using a dedicated random number key.

To access a tool at any time during a lesson, click on the **Math Tools icon** and **select the desired tool and mode** in the Math Tools window.

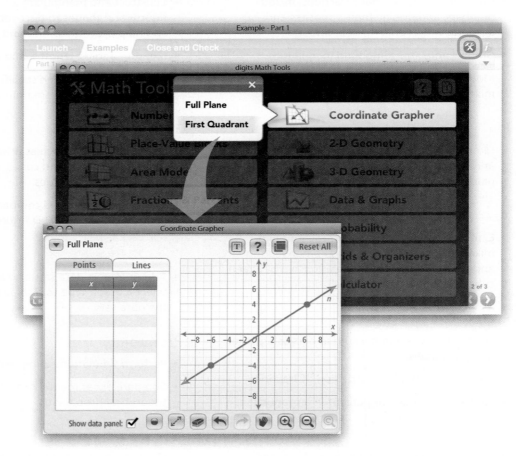

To open another copy of a tool with the current settings, simply **click on Copy** within the tool.

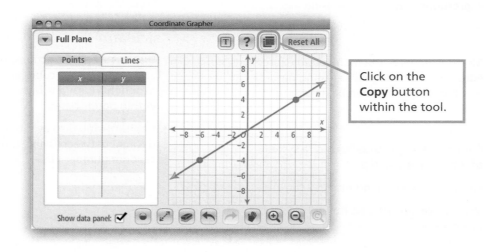

Click on the **Copy** button within the tool.

To access **video tutorials** on the Math Tools,
open the **Help** window and select a tool.

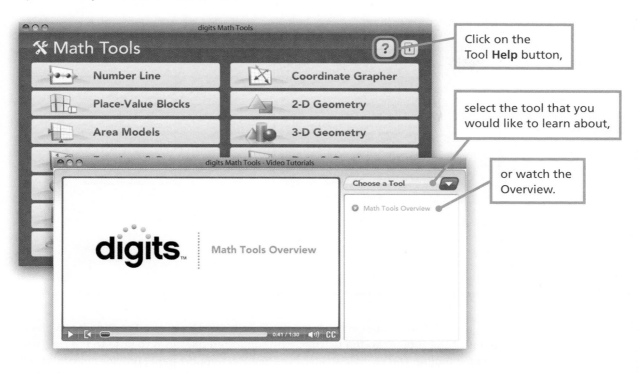

Click on the
Tool **Help** button,

select the tool that you
would like to learn about,

or watch the
Overview.

To access **video tutorials** for each individual tool, simply select the
desired tutorial after clicking on the **Help** button within the tool.

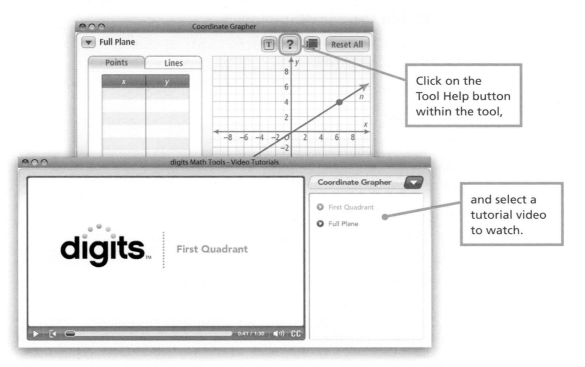

Click on the
Tool Help button
within the tool,

and select a
tutorial video
to watch.

Teaching Support

Clicking on the **Teacher Support** button opens the Teacher Support panel.

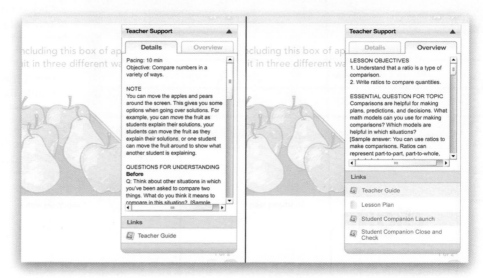

The Teacher Support panel has two tabs: **Details** and **Overview**. The Details tab gives point-of-use support to the teacher, with suggested questions to pose to the class for understanding. The Overview tab of the Teacher Support panel provides information on the objectives of the lesson, the essential question of the topic, the focus question of the lesson, and the author's intent. At the bottom of each tab is a set of links to relevant resources, such as the Teacher Guide and the student companion pages.

Teacher Guide Preparation Notes

The Teacher Guide provides detailed support for each lesson in the program. Elements of that support include:

- Lesson Objectives

- Focus Question

- Math Background

- Launch (with Author Intent, Questions for Understanding, and Solution Notes)

- Key Concept (with Questions for Understanding)

- Examples (with Author Intent, Questions for Understanding, Solutions Notes, and Got It Notes)

- Close and Check (with Focus Question Notes and Essential Question Connection)

- Various suggestions for Differentiated Instruction, Error Prevention, and comments on effective instruction through Interactivity

- Suggestions for using the hosts' commentary ("Jay says"), which supports the Focus and Essential Questions.

Icons used in the Teacher Guide indicate material of special interest:

© Common Core State Standards are referenced.

▦ Support for discussion of an Essential Question or a Focus Question, parts of embedded Understanding by Design strategies.

☞✦✧ An interactive mode is used to present this material.

⚒ One of 13 math tools is either suggested or already embedded in the presentation material.

Vocabulary and Key Concepts

Clicking on the **Vocabulary and Key Concepts** button opens a new window with the vocabulary and key concepts of the specific lesson that you are teaching pre-sorted in a list.

Spanish translation and other search options are built into the window. To review the vocabulary and key concepts from the previous lesson, simply select the lesson from the Lesson Vocabulary list.

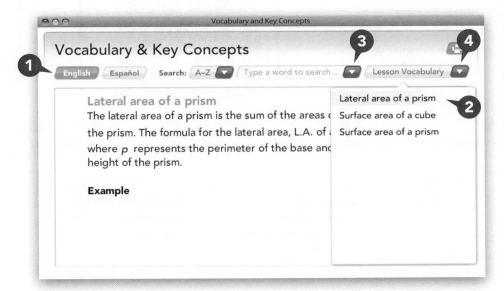

1. **Select** English or Spanish

2. **Select a term** in the list to view the definition or explanation

3. Type or select a **different term**

4. Select a **different lesson** to view its vocabulary and key concepts

Launch Features

The **Launch** problem is designed to:

- engage students immediately in math

- draw out prior knowledge

- and introduce the lesson concept.

Teachers can use the Launch as a "warm-up" that students complete independently or have the class work on it together using strategies that are most comfortable to the students. Launch problems are designed to enable student-oriented mathematical exploration and discourse for deeper conceptual understanding, both of which are proven to enhance understanding. Special features on the Launch screen include the **Work It Out, Companion Page,** and **Solution** buttons.

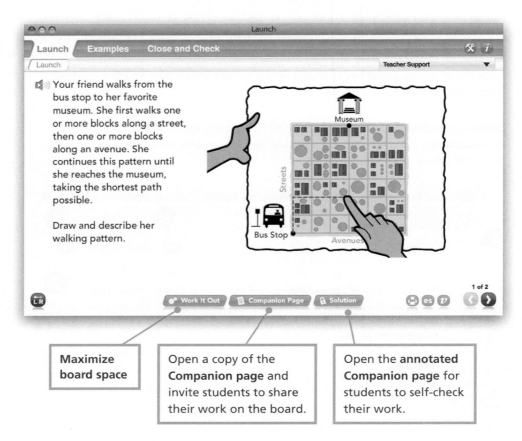

| Maximize board space | Open a copy of the **Companion page** and invite students to share their work on the board. | Open the **annotated Companion page** for students to self-check their work. |

The **Work It Out button** shrinks the text and images to maximize your board space for modeling a solution free hand or with Math Tools, or for inviting students to the board to share solutions. The Return button returns the problem statement and images to the original dimensions.

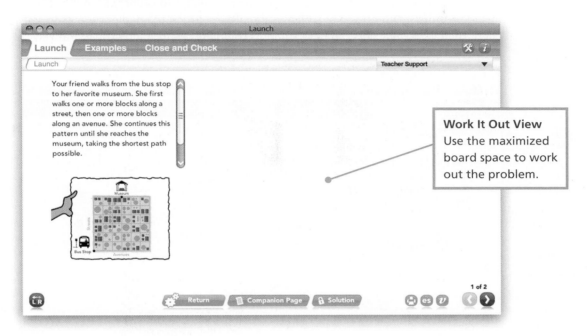

Each **Companion Page** provides work space to capture student reasoning and a Reflect question that either extends the problem or asks the student to reflect on their method of solving.

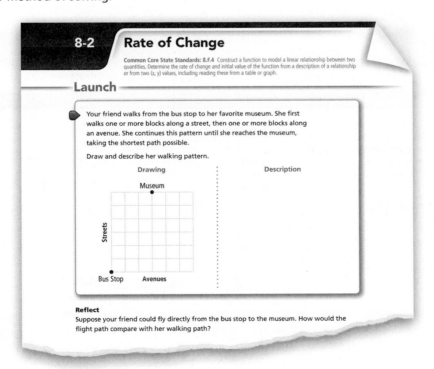

Examples Features

Examples provide explicit instruction of the lesson's concept and build upon one another in difficulty and conceptual development. Similar to Launch, Examples also include a Work It Out button as well as a complete **solution** to enable students to self check their work. Teachers can have students complete the examples collaboratively or independently.

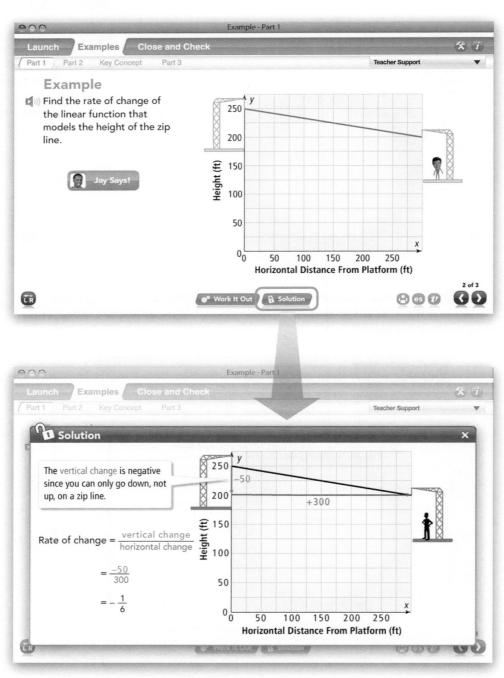

Each example concludes with a "**Got It?**" The "Got It?" feature is instructional assessment that teachers can use to determine whether or not the class understood the example. If students are successful with the "Got It?", the teacher can move on with confidence. If the class is not successful with the "Got It?," the teacher can re-teach the example immediately or make adjustments to the next example. Teachers can administer the "Got It?" in a variety of ways. On entry, the screen is designed with whitespace so that teachers can model a solution or invite students to the board. If the class has student response devices (clickers), the teacher can display multiple choice options.

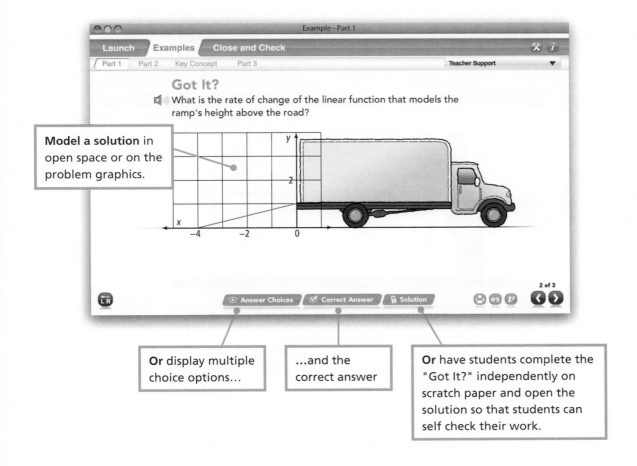

Model a solution in open space or on the problem graphics.

Or display multiple choice options...

...and the correct answer

Or have students complete the "Got It?" independently on scratch paper and open the solution so that students can self check their work.

Close and Check Features

The **Close and Check** is designed to bring students back to the Focus Question. Teachers can click on Work It Out to maximize board space for writing down class discourse or a summary of the lesson, open the companion page on screen to have students share solutions, or open an **annotated solution page** for students to self check their work.

The accompanying **Companion Page** includes "Do You Know How?," which are additional problems similar to the examples and "Do You Understand?" for higher order thinking.

Thus, the student companion becomes a student-created reference resource for when students are completing problems outside of class.

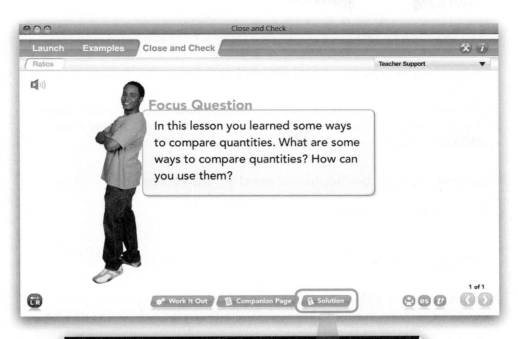

Focus Question

In this lesson you learned some ways to compare quantities. What are some ways to compare quantities? How can you use them?

1 of 1

Work It Out   Companion Page   Solution

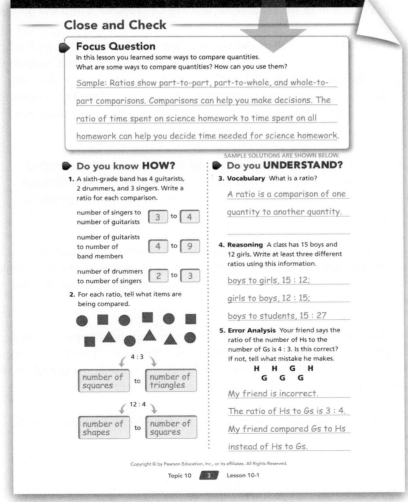

Close and Check

Focus Question

In this lesson you learned some ways to compare quantities.
What are some ways to compare quantities? How can you use them?

Sample: Ratios show part-to-part, part-to-whole, and whole-to-part comparisons. Comparisons can help you make decisions. The ratio of time spent on science homework to time spent on all homework can help you decide time needed for science homework.

SAMPLE SOLUTIONS ARE SHOWN BELOW.

Do you know HOW?

1. A sixth-grade band has 4 guitarists, 2 drummers, and 3 singers. Write a ratio for each comparison.

   number of singers to number of guitarists   [3] to [4]

   number of guitarists to number of band members   [4] to [9]

   number of drummers to number of singers   [2] to [3]

2. For each ratio, tell what items are being compared.

   4 : 3

   [number of squares] to [number of triangles]

   12 : 4

   [number of shapes] to [number of squares]

Do you UNDERSTAND?

3. **Vocabulary** What is a ratio?

   A ratio is a comparison of one quantity to another quantity.

4. **Reasoning** A class has 15 boys and 12 girls. Write at least three different ratios using this information.

   boys to girls, 15 : 12;

   girls to boys, 12 : 15;

   boys to students, 15 : 27

5. **Error Analysis** Your friend says the ratio of the number of Hs to the number of Gs is 4 : 3. Is this correct? If not, tell what mistake he makes.

   H H G H
   G G G

   My friend is incorrect.

   The ratio of Hs to Gs is 3 : 4.

   My friend compared Gs to Hs instead of Hs to Gs.

Topic 10   3   Lesson 10-1

◀ Annotated Solution Page

Homework and Assessments

Homework and Assessments in *digits* are powered by MathXL for School.

Homework has 2 parts: **Lesson Practice** and **Mixed Review**. Lesson practice includes problems that support the instruction of the corresponding lesson. Mixed Review contains exercises that address previously taught content.

Homework can be administered in three forms:

- ☑ Traditional paper-based
- ☑ From CD
- ☑ Online

Printable homework pdfs are provided on the teacher resource DVD to support paper-based homework. All pdfs are labeled with the lesson number and title for easy identification. After printing or duplication, students complete the assignment on paper and turn it in to the teacher for grading and recording into the gradebook.

The Homework CD contains all of the homework assignments labeled with lesson number and title. When using the CD, students select the appropriate assignment and complete through the MathXL interface, which includes access to learning aids. The assignment is automatically graded with results displayed on a summary screen that the student can print and turn in to his teacher for recording into the gradebook.

Homework online includes learning aids, auto-grading, and auto-reporting straight into the teacher's online gradebook. When students log in through My Math Universe, they will automatically see the appropriate assignments in their To Do list.

The learning aids have been shown to have significant impact on student performance. **Powered by MathXL,** *digits* learning aids include access to another example that is similar to the assigned problem, and an ability to step out the problem.

Help Me Solve This scaffolds the problem by asking a prompting question at each individual step. Students are provided with instant feedback for each step in order to address any misconceptions at the source. When the Help item is closed, the item algorithmically regenerates with new values for a fresh attempt.

View an Example provides a fully worked out step-by-step solution of a similar problem.

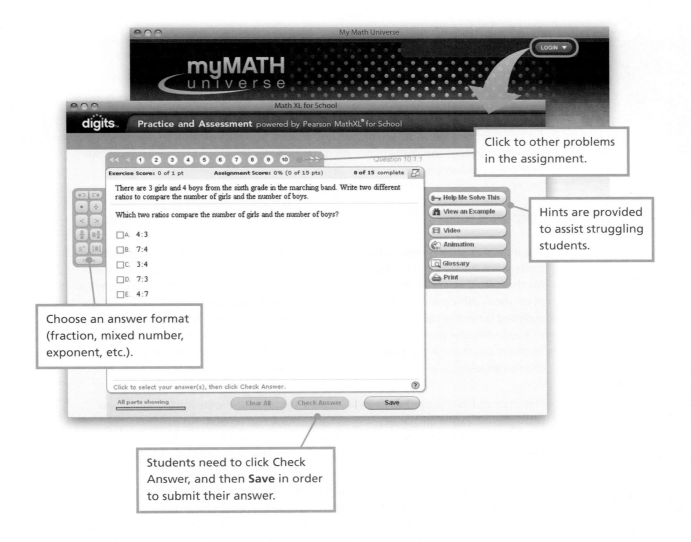

Click to other problems in the assignment.

Hints are provided to assist struggling students.

Choose an answer format (fraction, mixed number, exponent, etc.).

Students need to click Check Answer, and then **Save** in order to submit their answer.

Assessments can be administered on paper or online. Similar to paper-based homework, printable assessment pdfs are provided on the teacher resource DVD. For online delivery, after logging in, students immediately access the assessment from their To Do list when the teacher makes it available.

My Math Universe

The student website is **www.MyMathUniverse.com**. The website contains additional content that students can access prior to logging in. The purpose of this content is to provoke interest and engagement in math and provide additional preparation for the assignments. Since the site is mobile-enabled, students can access the assignment preparation materials while on the go, on any device. Once logged in, the student is able to access all class lessons and assignments, however, they can only be viewed on hardware that supports Adobe Flash.

Differentiating Instruction

Instruction in *digits* is automatically differentiated with Readiness Lessons designed for small groups, daily differentiated homework, and Intervention Lessons assigned through personalized study plans. All differentiation is driven by the results of the Readiness Assessments.

Learner Levels and Study Plans

The Readiness Assessment determines a student's proficiency with pre-requisite content for a unit of instruction. The overall score sets the student's Learner Level for the unit. By default, the Learner Level threshold is 70%. Students with scores at or above 70% are identified as proficient with the pre-requisite content and are assigned G for the Learner Level. Students with scores below 70% are identified as weak with the pre-requisite content and are assigned K for the Learner Level. Teachers can change the Learner Level threshold if desired. Additionally, teachers can change an individual student's Learner Level assignment.

The Learner Level is used to determine how to group students for the Readiness Lesson. The teacher provides pre-requisite instruction to students assigned the K Learner Level (and may include G Learner Level students as well) and distributes the Readiness Lesson activity sheets according to the Learner Level assignments.

The Learner Level also enables the automatic assignment of differentiated online homework throughout the unit. Students assigned the G Learner Level automatically receive homework that includes exercises with increased challenge. Students assigned the K Learner Level automatically receive homework that includes exercises that help them develop mathematical thinking.

In addition to setting the Learner Levels, the Readiness Assessment data is also evaluated to identify specific areas of prerequisite weakness for each student. Personalized study plans with intervention content are generated according to this evaluation.

The **Learner Level Settings** can be reviewed and modified through the gradebook. If the Readiness Assessment is not assigned to students, all students are assigned to Learner Level G.

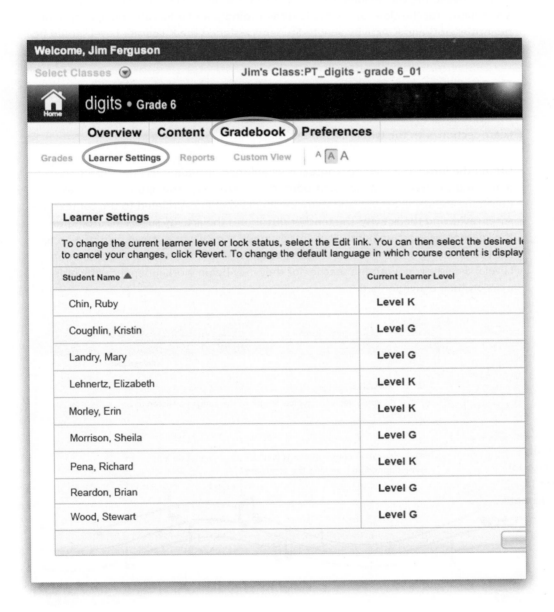

Delivering Readiness Lessons

Prior to delivering the Readiness Lesson, teachers should review the Learner Level assignments for the class, group students accordingly, and duplicate the appropriate quantities of G and K Activity Sheets. Students assigned the K Learner Level should be situated together in close proximity to the interactive whiteboard or screen.

The **Readiness Lesson** has three major parts: **Intro**, **Learn**, and **Close**. The Intro and Close are whole class exchanges, whereas Learn provides additional instruction on the unit's pre-requisites for students assigned Learner Level K. Teachers may use the Learn section with the whole class if desired.

During the **Intro**, a real-world context is established, including its relationship to math, and the lesson's activity is introduced. Students have the opportunity to ask questions about the activity and share personal experiences related to the context. After reviewing the activity, the teacher distributes the activity sheets according to the Learner Level assignments. Students assigned the K Learner Level continue on to the Learn segment of the lesson with the teacher. Students assigned the G Learner Level may also work with the teacher, or they may begin work independently or in pairs on their activity sheets.

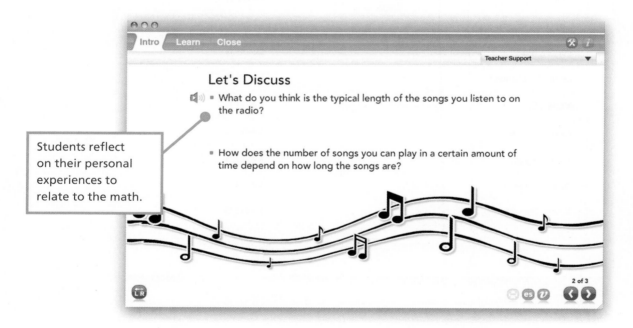

Students reflect on their personal experiences to relate to the math.

Learn provides additional explicit instruction on the pre-requisite content. Examples illustrate the use of various mathematical concepts and skills in the world context of the lesson. Teachers can model solutions, invite students to the board to solve using various strategies, or display fully worked out solutions.

After working through the examples, students work independently or in pairs within their Learner Level group on their activity sheets. Since students assigned the G Learner Level demonstrated proficiency on the pre-requisite content, the G activity sheet focuses on extending students' understanding with additional challenge. The K activity sheet provides additional scaffolding to support students with weakness in the pre-requisite content.

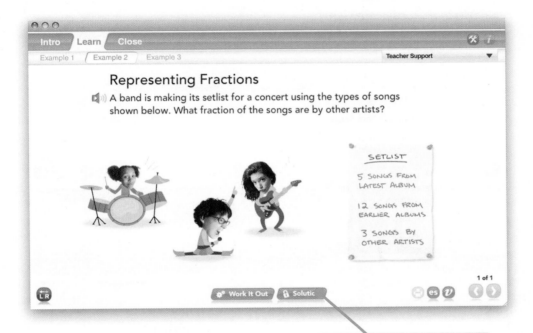

Flexible features provide different ways to present solutions.

The whole class is brought together for the **Close**. Students share findings or solutions, discuss various strategies, and explain their reasoning. Because the real world context is common, all students are able to contribute and benefit from the discourse.

Students share and compare solutions and strategies and verbalize reasoning.

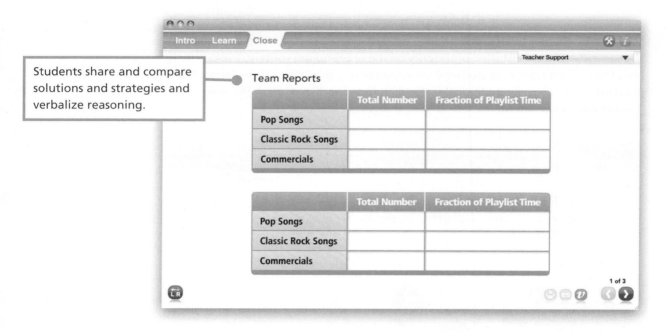

A summary of the prerequisite content is reviewed to ensure that all students are prepared for the upcoming unit of instruction.

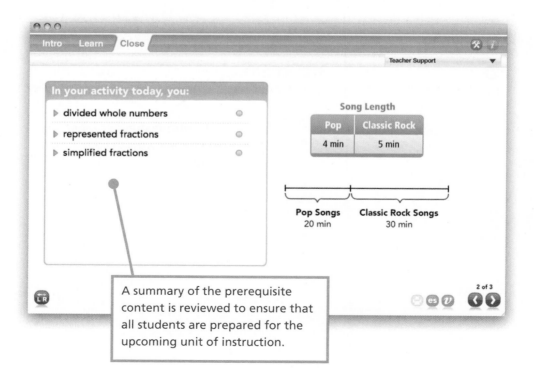

Delivering Intervention Lessons

Intervention in *digits* is designed to support various implementation models. Intervention lessons can be completed by students independently or can be completed with the guidance of a teacher. Research indicates that students who are on grade level with occasional areas of weakness are able to complete intervention independently, whereas students with large gaps in understanding are best served with additional teacher guidance in a small group setting, such as in an intervention pull-out or a Title 1 class.

At the start of every unit, teachers should conference with each student to discuss the study plan and provide pacing guidance. Teachers may decide to provide students with incremental milestone dates to assist with pacing. To complete intervention lessons, students need to be online and have access to a printer. After students log in on My Math Universe, they can access an assigned Readiness Assessment. This assessment will generate a Study Plan with appropriate Intervention Lessons. Each Intervention Lesson has an accompanying **Journal page**, which provides students with a scaffolded resource to complete a Got It? for each example and to complete the Lesson Check. Students should print out the Journal page before entering the lesson.

Intervention Lessons have two parts: **Examples** and **Lesson Check**. The Examples provide explicit instruction, an opportunity to try a problem with scaffolding and a solution, and a Got It? problem to assess understanding.

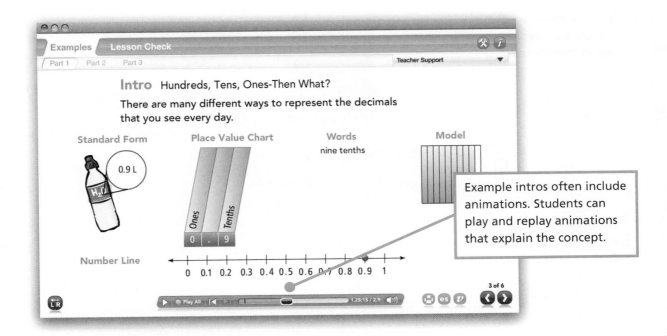

Example intros often include animations. Students can play and replay animations that explain the concept.

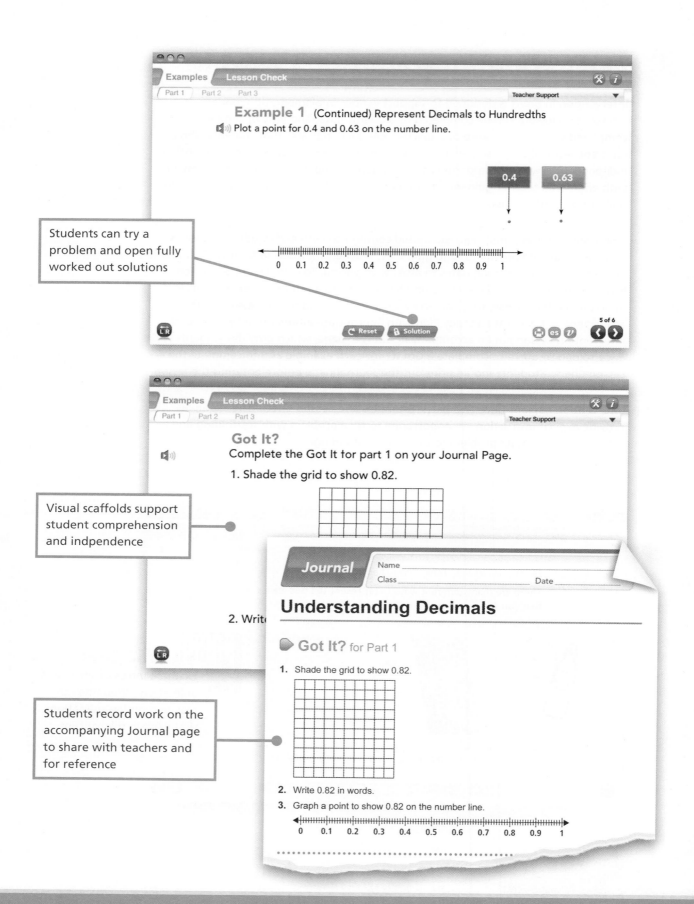

Students can try a problem and open fully worked out solutions

Visual scaffolds support student comprehension and indpendence

Students record work on the accompanying Journal page to share with teachers and for reference

The **Lesson Check** reviews the Key Concept and provides additional problems similar to the examples in the Do You Know How section, and questions that promote reasoning in the Do You Understand section.

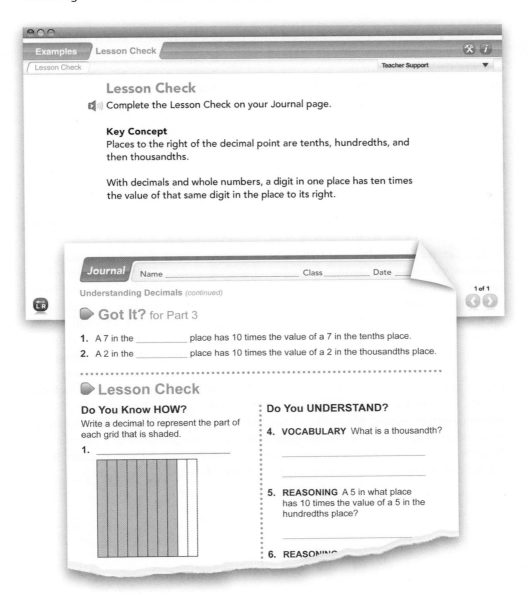

Every Intervention Lesson is paired with automatically graded practice exercises that provide teachers with quantitative data on students' understanding of the intervention content.

Assigning a Topic Test with Study Plan

Summative Topic Tests are available with and without study plans. When students take a Topic Test with study plan, they are assigned Key Concepts and additional practice from the lessons that cover any areas of weakness in the topic. Before assigning a Topic Test with study plan, teachers should examine students' work load to ensure that they are not overwhelmed with assignments.

Challenging Gifted Students

Enrichment activities in *digits* are unit-based opportunities to further assess students' understanding of the math concepts of a unit using research and creativity. Each activity presents a situation or problem to investigate. The student is expected to organize, plan, research, write, and present his or her results. The presentation of results is an extended written response, supported by visuals that may take the form of a game, a model, an interactive whiteboard presentation, a poster, or brochure. Each enrichment activity has a student support page to describe the situation, provide guidelines for each stage of the activity, a project checklist as the activity is completed, and the scoring rubric. The teacher support page offers prompting questions to introduce the activity, suggestions for implementation, supporting questions for key stages in the activity, and additional challenge activities to further expand the project. The enrichment activities were designed to support various implementation models. Students can complete enrichment activities independently, by working in groups, or as a whole-class project with the guidance of a teacher. There is also flexibility on the timing of the activities. Enrichment activities can be assigned at the start of a unit or at any time during the work in a unit.

Weather or Not

Getting Started

Would you go swimming in 32° water? Is -2° a good temperature setting for a home freezer? The answer to both questions is, "That depends!" Are you using the Celsius or Fahrenheit scale? Water at 32° C feels like a bath! As for a freezer, -2°F is a deep freeze! People living in North America use both the Fahrenheit and Celsius scales, so it pays to know the difference.

For this project, you will examine weather data for a state or region of your choice. Your final project will be a report on temperature data, using both scales.

Activities

Organizing

Create a chart that compares the Celsius and Fahrenheit temperature scales. Indicate real-life situations, such as snowstorms, boiling water, and beach weather. Include the chart in your report. What temperature is the same on both scales? Does this temperature ever occur in the region covered by your report?

Researching

For the state, country, or region you select, research the historic temperature extremes. Report on the highest and lowest temperatures ever recorded. Include data on monthly or seasonal highs and lows as well. Be sure to use reliable sources to collect your data.

Modeling

Develop a simple rule for mentally estimating the  given the Celsius temperature. Give the rule in w include it in your report.

Writing

The Fahrenheit scale is widely used in the United scientists almost always use the Celsius scale in so, and include your explanation in your report.

TEACHER NOTES: Weather or Not

About the Project

This project allows students to apply their knowledge of integers to weather data.

Introducing the Project

Ask students:

- Do you pay attention to weather data? What trends do you notice?
- How do temperatures vary during a day and during the year for our area of the country?
- How can weather data be used to make predictions about the weather?

Activity 1: Organizing

Pick two events. Find the difference between the temperatures on both scales. Use tables and graphs to record the temperatures. Ask students:

- Which scale had the greater difference?
- What does the change in temperature mean?

Activity 2: Researching

Students can find extreme temperatures in almanacs, on the Internet, or from the meteorologist at a local news station.

Activity 3: Modeling

Students should look at the temperature comparison scales they drew for Activity 1 of the project.

Activity 4: Writing

Ask students:

- At what temperature does water boil in degrees Fahrenheit and degrees Celsius?
- At what temperature does water freeze in degrees Fahrenheit and degrees Celsius?
- Which scale do you think is easier to use? Explain your reasoning.

Challenge Activity: Temperatures other than Fahrenheit and Celsius

Supporting English Language Learners

English Language Learners in the Math Classroom

English language learners share many characteristics with other students, but they also need support and scaffolding that are specific to them. Why? Because they represent a highly diverse population. They come from many home language backgrounds and cultures. They have a wide range of prior educational and numeracy experiences in their home languages. And they come to school with varying levels of English language proficiency and experience with mainstream U.S. culture.

Helping English language learners acquire content mastery is not enough. English language learners are also expected to participate in yearly high-stakes tests. Research has consistently shown that ELLs usually require at least five years, on average, to catch up to native-speaker norms in academic language proficiency (Cummins, 1981).

The following pages have been designed to help you identify and respond appropriately to the varying needs of ELLs in your classroom. They provide insight on how to help ELLs develop fluency as readers, writers, listeners, and speakers of academic English, while learning mathematical concepts at the same time. In addition, they offer strategies and activities to help you scaffold and support ELL instruction so that all your students can learn in ways that are comprehensible and meaningful, and in ways that promote academic success and achievement.

English Language Learners

Dr. Jim Cummins

Dr. Jim Cummins is Professor and Canada Research Chair in the Centre for Educational Research on Languages and Literacies, part of the Ontario Institute for Studies in Education of the University of Toronto. His research focuses on literacy development in multilingual school contexts as well as on the potential roles of technology in promoting language and literacy development. Jim is actively working on two books that (hopefully) will appear in 2011. One is tentatively titled Pedagogies of Choice for English Language Learners and the other Identity Texts: The Collaborative Creation of Power in Multilingual School Contexts.

Mathematics and Language

Mathematics can legitimately be considered a language in itself in that it employs symbols to represent concepts and operations that facilitate our thinking about aspects of reality. However, mathematics is also intimately related to the natural language that we begin to acquire as infants, the language that we use to communicate in a variety of everyday and academic contexts. Mathematics and language are interconnected at several levels:

- Teachers use natural language to explain mathematical concepts and perform mathematical operations. Students who have limited proficiency in English require additional support in order to understand mathematical concepts and operations taught in English. Among the supports that teachers can use to make instruction comprehensible for English learners are demonstrations using concrete, hands-on manipulatives; graphic organizers; simplification and paraphrasing of instructional language; and direct teaching of key vocabulary.

- As is the case in other academic disciplines, mathematics uses a specialized technical vocabulary to represent concepts and describe operations. Students are required to learn the meanings of such words as *congruence*, *ratio*, *integer*, and *quotient*, words that are likely to be found only in mathematics discourse. Furthermore, other terms have specific meanings in mathematics discourse that differ from their meanings in everyday usage and in other subject areas. Examples of these kinds of terms include words such as *table*, *product*, *even*, and *odd*. Homophones such as sum and some may also be confusing for ELL students. Grade 6 students are required to learn concepts such as least common multiple when ELL students may not know the broader meanings of the words *least* and *common*.

- In addition to the technical vocabulary of mathematics, language intersects with mathematics at the broader level of general vocabulary, syntax, semantics, and discourse. Most mathematical problems require students to understand propositions and logical relations that are expressed through language. Consider this problem at the Grade 6 level:

  A baseball team won 36 games this season, 6 fewer games than last season. Solve the equation n − 6 = 36 to find n, the number of games they won last season.

  Here students need to understand (or be able to figure out) the meanings of such words as *equation* and *season*. They need to understand the logical relation expressed by the fewer … than … construction. And they need to infer that the team played more than 36 games last season, even though this fact is not explicitly included in the problem. Clearly, the language demands of the math curriculum increase as students progress through the grades, and these demands can cause particular difficulties for ELL students.

The Challenges of Academic Language

The intersection of language and content entails both challenges and opportunities in teaching English language learners. It is clearly challenging to teach complex math content to students whose knowledge of English academic language may be considerably below the level assumed by the curriculum and textbooks. In a typical math lesson, for example, several difficult words may be explained in the margins. However, there may be many more words in each lesson that are new to ELL students. These gaps in their knowledge of academic language are likely to seriously impede their understanding of the text.

Students may also be unfamiliar with grammatical constructions and typical conventions of academic writing that are present in the text. For example, academic texts frequently use passive voice, whereas we rarely use this construction in everyday conversation. Also, students are often given writing assignments to demonstrate their understanding.

- **Clarify Language (Paraphrase Ideas, Enunciate Clearly, Adjust Speech Rate, and Simplify Sentences)** This category includes a variety of strategies and language-oriented activities that clarify the meanings of new words and concepts. Teachers can modify their language to students by *paraphrasing ideas* and by *explaining new concepts and words*. They can explain new words by providing synonyms, antonyms, and definitions either in English or in the home language of students, if they know it. Important vocabulary can be repeated and recycled as part of the paraphrasing of ideas. Teachers should speak in a natural rhythm, but enunciate clearly and adjust their speech to a rate that ELL students will find easier to understand. Meaning can also be communicated and/or reinforced through gesture, body language, and demonstrations. Because of their common roots in Latin and Greek, much of the technical math vocabulary in English has cognates in Romance languages such as Spanish (e.g., *addition—adición*). Students who know these languages can be encouraged to make cross-linguistic linkages as a means of reinforcing the concept. Bilingual and English-only dictionaries can also be useful tools for language clarification, particularly for intermediate-grade students.

- **Give Frequent Feedback and Expand Student Responses** *Giving frequent feedback* means responding positively and naturally to all forms of responses. Teachers can let their students know how they are doing by responding to both their words and their actions. Teachers can also assess their students' understanding by asking them to give examples, or by asking them how they would explain a concept or idea to someone else. *Expanding student responses* often means using polar (either/or) questions with students who are just beginning to produce oral English and 5 W (who, what, when, where, why) questions with students who are more fluent. Teachers can easily, and casually, expand their students' one- and two-word answers into complete sentences ("Yes, a triangle has one base") and respond to grammatically incorrect answers by recasting them using standard English syntax (Student: "I gotted 4 and 19 thousandths"; Teacher: "That's right, you have 4 and 19 thousandths").

Opportunities for Extending Language

Content teachers are usually acutely aware of the challenges of teaching ELL students within the subject-matter classroom. However, they may be less aware of the opportunities that exist for extending students' knowledge of academic English. Students who are learning math are also learning the language of math. They are learning that there are predictable patterns in the ways we form abstract nouns that describe mathematical processes. For example, many of these nouns are formed by adding the suffix *-tion* to the verb, as in *add/addition, estimate/estimation,* etc.

Similarly, when students report back to the class on their observations of a problem-solving exercise or project, teachers have the opportunity to model the kinds of explicit formal language that is required to talk and write about mathematical operations. The feedback they provide to students on their oral or written assignments clarifies not only the mathematical concepts that students are learning but also the language forms, functions, and conventions that are required to discuss these concepts. Thus, math teachers are also language teachers and have significant opportunities to extend students' ability to understand and use academic language.

Without strong writing skills in English, ELL students will find it difficult to demonstrate content knowledge.

Obviously, teachers focus their instruction on explaining concepts to students, but ELL students may not yet have acquired the English proficiency to understand explanations that are accessible to native speakers of the language. Thus, a major challenge for teachers is to teach content effectively to *all* students, particularly those who are not yet fully proficient in English. Although this challenge is formidable, particularly at the intermediate level, teachers can draw on a knowledge base of recent research findings in order to implement instructional approaches that have proved highly effective in enabling ELL students to gain access to academic content.

> " The number of **ELLs** has grown rapidly in the last 15 years to about **5 million students**. Estimates project this number **will increase 100%** to 10 million, **by 2015**. "
>
> —*NEA 2008*

Access Content

Activating and building students' background knowledge is an essential part of the process of helping students to participate academically and gain access to meaning. When we activate students' prior knowledge, we attempt to modify the "soil" so that the seeds of meaning can take root. However, we can also support or *scaffold* students' learning by modifying the input itself. We provide this scaffolding by embedding the content in a *richly redundant context* wherein there are multiple routes to the mathematical meaning at hand in addition to the language itself. The following list presents a variety of ways of modifying the presentation of mathematical content to ELL students so that they can more effectively get access to the meaning in any given lesson.

- **Use Demonstration** Teachers can take students through a word problem in math, demonstrating step-by-step procedures and strategies in a clear and explicit manner.

- **Use Manipulatives (and Tools and Technology)** In the early grades, manipulatives may include counters and blocks that enable students to carry out a mathematical operation, literally with their hands, and actually see the concrete results of that operation. At the intermediate level, measuring tools, such as rulers and protractors, and technological aids, such as calculators and computers, will be used. The effectiveness of these tools will be enhanced, if they are used within the context of a project that students are intrinsically motivated to initiate and complete.

- **Use Small-Group Interactions and Peer Questioning** Working either as a whole class or in heterogeneous groups or pairs, students can engage in real-life or simulated projects that require application of a variety of mathematical skills.

- **Use Pictures, Real Objects, and Graphic Organizers** We commonly hear the expression "A picture is worth a thousand words." There is a lot of truth to this when it comes to teaching academic content. Visuals enable students to "see" the basic concept we are trying to teach much more effectively than if we rely only on words. Once students grasp the concept, they are much more likely to be able to figure out the meanings of the words we use to talk about it. Among the visuals we can use in presenting math content are these: *pictures/photographs, real objects, graphic organizers, drawings on overhead projectors, and blackline masters.* Graphic organizers are particularly useful because they can be used not only by teachers to present concepts but also by students to take notes, organize their ideas in logical categories, and summarize the results of group brainstorming on particular issues.

The Knowledge Base

There is considerable agreement among researchers about the general patterns of academic development among ELL students and the factors that support students in catching up academically. The following findings are well-established:

The language of academic success in school is very different from the language we use in everyday conversational interactions. Face-to-face conversational interactions are supported by facial expressions, eye contact, gestures, intonation, and the immediate concrete context. Conversational interactions among native-speakers draw on a core set of high-frequency words (approximately 2,000) and use a limited set of grammatical constructions and discourse conventions. Academic language, by contrast, draws on a much larger set of low-frequency words, including both general academic words and the specific technical vocabulary of a particular content area (e.g., *coordinate plane, triangular prism,* etc.). This language is found predominantly in two places—classrooms and texts (both printed and electronic).

ELL students typically require at least five years to catch up academically to native speakers; by contrast, basic conversational fluency is usually acquired within 1–2 years. These trajectories reflect both the increased linguistic complexity of academic language and the fact that ELL students are attempting to catch up to a moving target. Students whose first language is English are not standing still waiting for ELL students to catch up. Every year, they make gains in reading, writing, and vocabulary abilities. So, ELL students have to learn faster to bridge the gap. The fact that at least five years is typically required for ELL students to catch up academically highlights the urgency of providing academic and linguistic support to students *across the curriculum.* Ideally, ELL teachers and subject-matter teachers will work together to enable ELL students to develop the academic language skills they need to access subject-matter content and succeed academically.

All learning builds on a foundation of preexisting knowledge and skills. For ELL students in the early stages of learning English, this conceptual foundation is likely to be encoded predominantly in their home language (L1). This finding implies that students' L1 is potentially relevant to learning English academic skills and concepts. Students' L1 is the cognitive tool they have used to interact with the world and learn academic content. Thus, rather than ignoring students' L1, we should consider teaching for transfer across languages and encourage students to use their L1 as a stepping stone to higher performance in English academic tasks.

The Pearson ELL Curriculum Framework

The core principles of teaching ELL students across the curriculum are outlined in The Pearson ELL Curriculum Framework. This framework was designed to assist content-area teachers in addressing the needs of the growing and diverse English language learner population. The five principles in the outer circle of the framework represent the ways in which the teacher plans and organizes the delivery of instruction. The three processes in the inner circle highlight what teachers attempt to do in direct interaction with their students. As depicted in the diagram, these principles and processes flow into each other and represent components or phases of a dynamic whole.

1 Identify and Communicate Content and Language Objectives
In planning and organizing a lesson, teachers must first identify what content and language objectives they will attempt to communicate to students.

2 Frontload the Lesson
Frontloading refers to the use of prereading or preinstructional strategies that prepare English language learners to understand new academic content. It involves strategies such as activating prior knowledge, building background, previewing text, preteaching vocabulary, and making connections.

3 Provide Comprehensible Input
Language and content that students can understand is referred to as comprehensible input. Teachers make use of nonlinguistic supports to enable students to understand language and content that would otherwise have been beyond their comprehension. Typical supports or "scaffolds" include graphic organizers, photographs, illustrations, models, demonstrations, outlines, etc. Language clarification and use of paraphrasing also contribute to making the input comprehensible.

4 Enable Language Production Language production complements comprehensible input and is an essential element in developing expertise in academic language. Use of both oral and written language enables students to solve problems, generate insights, express their ideas and identities, and obtain feedback from teachers and peers.

5 Assess for Content and Language Understanding Finally, the instructional cycle flows into assessing what students have learned and then spiraling upwards into further development of students' content knowledge and language expertise.

Classroom Interactions

When we shift into the actual classroom interactions that this lesson cycle generates, a primary focus is on the extent to which teachers' interactions with students motivate them to engage academically. Promotion of motivation and engagement represents a process of negotiating identities between teachers and students. Students who feel their culture and personal identity validated in the classroom are much more likely to engage with academic content than those who perceive that their culture and identity are ignored or devalued. An excellent way of enabling ELL students to take pride in their academic accomplishments is to encourage (or require) them to undertake challenging project work while providing the support to enable them to complete the task successfully.

Differentiation of instruction is widely accepted as necessary to address the learning needs of a diverse school population. One-size-fits-all programs typically exclude ELL students from meaningful participation. When applied to ELL students, differentiation involves scaffolding of input to students and output from students. Activating prior knowledge and building background knowledge is one example of a differentiation/scaffolding strategy.

Assessment and intervention are fused into the cycle of motivating students and providing differentiated instruction that addresses the background knowledge and learning needs of individual students. It is essential that teachers regularly assess the extent to which ELL students understand the content presented through classroom instruction and in the textbook. If not, many students who are still in the process of learning academic English may grasp only a fraction of this content. This formative assessment represents an ongoing process in the classroom and, in comparison to most standardized tests, gives the teacher information that is immediately relevant to intervention and further scaffolding of instruction.

Conclusion

The knowledge base that research has generated about ELL students' academic trajectories shows clearly that ELL students must be understanding instruction and learning English across the curriculum if they are to catch up in time to meet graduation requirements. Teaching mathematics affords opportunities for extending ELL students' academic language proficiency. The Pearson ELL Curriculum Framework incorporates the essential elements that teachers need to implement effective instruction for all students—English-language and native English-speaking learners alike.

References for Foundational Research

Anthony, A.R. (2008). Output strategies for English language learners: Theory to Practice. *The Reading Teacher, 61(6)*, 472–482.

August, D., & Shanahan, T. (Eds.) (2006). *Developing literacy in second-language learners: Report of the National Literacy Panel on Language-Minority Children and Youth*. Executive Summary.

Barrera, R.B., & Jimenez, R.T. (2000). *Literacy instruction for bilingual Latino students: Teachers' experiences and knowledge*. Office for Bilingual Education and Minority Language Affairs, Washington, DC.

Beilenberg, B., & Fillmore, L.W. (2004). The English they need for the test. *Educational Leadership, 62(4)*, 45–49.

Collier, V. & Thomas, W. (2002). *A national study of school effectiveness for language minority students' long-term academic achievement*. Santa Cruz, CA & Washington, DC: Center for Research on Education, Diversity & Excellence. Available: http://www.crede.ucsc.edu/research/llaa/1.1_final.html.

Cummins, J. (2005). Affirming identity in multilingual classrooms. *Educational Leadership, 63(1)*, 38–43.

Cummins, J. (2005). A proposal for action: Strategies for recognizing heritage language competence as a learning resource within the mainstream classroom. *The Modern Language Journal*, 89, 585–592.

Cummins, J. (1999). BICS and CALP: Clarifying the distinction. *Working papers on bilingualism*, 20.

Cummins, J. (1981). The role of primary language development in promoting educational success for language minority students. In *Schooling and language minority students: A theoretical framework*. Sacramento, CA: California Department of Education.

Fillmore, L.W. (2007). English learners and mathematics learning: Language issues to consider. In *Assessing mathematical proficiency*. MSRI Publications, Vol 53. library.msri.org/books/Book53/files/19fillmore.pdf

Fillmore, L.W. & Snow, C.E. (2000). *What teachers need to know about language*. ERIC Special Report.

Garcia, G.E. (1992). *The literacy assessment of second-language learners*. Center for the Study of Reading, University of Illinois Urbana-Champaign. Available on ERIC.

Garcia, G.E. (1994). Supporting second-language literacy: Enhancing the English literacy development of students who are learning English as a second language. *Illinois Reading Council Journal*. 22(1). Special Supplement.

Garcia, G.E. & Bauer, E.B. (2002). Lessons from a classroom teacher's use of alternative literacy assessment. *Research in the Teaching of English, 36(May)*.

Garcia, G.E. & Godina, H. (1994). *Bilingual preschool children's participation in classroom literacy activities: "Once Upon a Time" and its alternatives*. Paper presented at the Annual Meeting of the National Reading Conference.

Garcia, G.E. & McCarthy, S.J. (2005). English language learners writing practices and attitudes. *Written Communication, 22(1)*.

Garcia, G.E. & Pearson, P.D. (1990). *Modifying reading instruction to maximize its effectiveness for all students*. Technical Report #489. Center for the Study of Reading, University of Illinois Urbana-Champaign.

Jimenez, R.T. (2002). Key research, policy, and practice issues for fostering the literacy development of Latino students. *Focus on Exceptional Children, 34(6)*, 1–10.

Jimenez, R.T., Garcia, G.E., & Pearson, P.D. (1996). The reading strategies of bilingual Latino/a students who are successful English readers: Opportunities and obstacles. *Reading Research Quarterly, 31(1)*, 90–106.

Kieffer, M.J. & Lesaux, N.K. (2007). Breaking down words to build meaning: Morphology, vocabulary, and reading comprehension in the urban classroom. *The Reading Teacher*, 61, 134-144.

Leos, K., (2004). *No child left behind*. Paper presented at the annual conference of the National Association for Bilingual Education, Albuquerque, NM.

National Clearinghouse for English Language Acquisition, (2008). *Educating English language learners: Building teacher capacity*. Washington, DC: http://www.ncela.gwu.edu/practice/mainstream/volume_1.pdf.

National Clearinghouse for English Language Acquisition, (2008). How many school-aged limited English proficient (LEP) students are there in the U.S.? Washington, DC. http//www.ncela.gwu.edu/expert/faq/01leps.html.

National Education Association, (2008). *Campaign Briefing Book. Washington*, DC: http://educationvotes.nea.org/userfiles/08%20CampaignBrief–bw.pdf.

Schleppegrell, M. J., Achugar, M., & Oteiza, (2004). The grammar of history: Enhancing content-based instruction through a functional focus on language. *TESOL Quarterly, 38(1)*, 67–93.

Short, D., Crandall, J., & Christian, D., (1989). *How to integrate language and content instruction: A training manual*. The Center for Applied Linguistics.

Short, D. & Echevarria, J. (2004). Teacher skills to support English language learners. *Educational Leadership 62(4)*.

Five Essential Principles for Building ELL Lessons

PRINCIPLE 1

Identify and Communicate Content and Language Objectives

Content Objectives

Effective educational practices, as well as state and federal mandates, require that English language learners meet grade-level standards. The first step in reaching these standards is clearly targeting and communicating the content objectives of a lesson. While the content objectives for English language learners are the same as for mainstream learners, the objectives must be presented in language that suits the students' levels of language proficiency. This involves using simpler sentence structures and vocabulary, paraphrasing, repeating, and avoiding idioms and slang.

Language Objectives

Language objectives focus on promoting English language development while learning content. They can be thought of as a scaffold to help students learn content objectives. Language objectives include: content vocabulary, academic vocabulary, and language form and function.

Content vocabulary These terms are the specialized vocabulary of a subject area. Content vocabulary can be particularly challenging for English language learners who come from a variety of school backgrounds. ELLs should receive explicit instruction of key vocabulary words. Studies show that with this instruction, students are more likely to understand new words encountered during reading.

Academic vocabulary These terms can be described as "school language," or the language that students encounter across all subjects as opposed to the informal English words and structures used in conversation. Academic vocabulary includes words such as *similar, demonstrate, explain*, and *survey*. Research indicates that acquiring a strong grasp of academic vocabulary is a vital factor distinguishing successful students from those who struggle in school. Becoming fluent in academic language will enable English language learners to understand and analyze, write clearly about their ideas, and comprehend subject-area material.

Language form and function Language *forms* include sentence structure and grammar. Language *functions* involve the purpose of language (such as identifying or comparing). The language forms and functions students need to complete academic tasks should be taught within the context of the lesson. To develop appropriate form and function objectives, teachers can use standards developed for ELLs or coordinate with staff who specialize in language development. For example, when teaching *greater than/less than*, the language objective might be the structures for comparison (*-er* and *less*) and the function of how to make comparisons.

Teaching Strategies and Support for Principle 1

There are a number of basic strategies teachers can implement to meet the needs of their English language learners. Many are commonsense, everyday strategies that teachers in all content areas already know and use. These strategies lay the foundation for a positive learning relationship between student and teacher.

☐ **Previous lesson objectives** Begin each lesson with a review of the previous lesson's objectives.

☐ **Content objectives** Present the content objectives using visual aids, graphic organizers, and paraphrasing. Write the objectives on the board.

☐ **Prior knowledge** Ask students to talk about the content based on their prior knowledge. Document the results of the discussion with a graphic organizer.

☐ **Content and academic vocabulary** Present content and academic vocabulary.

- Pronounce the word and have students repeat.
- Provide examples, descriptions, visuals, and explanations.
- Clarify the part of speech and discuss cognates, synonyms, and antonyms.
- Ask students to provide examples, descriptions, visuals, and explanations of their own to determine comprehension.

☐ **Vocabulary notebooks** Have students keep a vocabulary notebook. Suggest that they use their own words to define the terms and incorporate visuals whenever possible.

☐ **Word-analysis strategies** Teach students word-analysis strategies so that new words can be attacked independently. For example, teach the prefix and the root of a vocabulary word. Write the meaning of the prefix and the root word on the board and have students do the same in their vocabulary notebooks.

☐ **Academic vocabulary practice** Provide flashcards or flashcard frames for key academic vocabulary. Have students use them for paired or independent practice, both during the week and for subsequent reviews. Encourage students to add personal notes and pictures to their flashcards.

☐ **Vocabulary practice** Design assignments so that students practice using the new words.

☐ **Language objectives** With the cooperation of an ESOL teacher, provide language objectives at different proficiency levels.

☐ **Opportunities for language objectives** If the lesson's content includes idioms or colloquialisms use these as opportunities to teach language objectives.

☐ **Lesson objectives review** End each lesson with a review of the lesson's content and language objectives and a preview of the next lesson's objectives.

Applying Principle 1 in *digits*

In the Lessons Readiness lessons help teachers assess student preparedness, while other lessons introduce concepts and explain problem solving. Intervention lessons provide additional support. For each lesson, an Overview can be found in the **Teacher Support** menu that provides the lesson objectives. Present these objectives before beginning the lesson. If necessary, rewrite them in simpler language and post them on the board. ▶

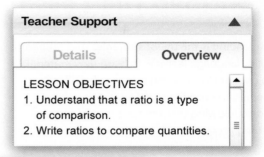

Teacher Support ▲

Details	Overview

LESSON OBJECTIVES
1. Understand that a ratio is a type of comparison.
2. Write ratios to compare quantities.

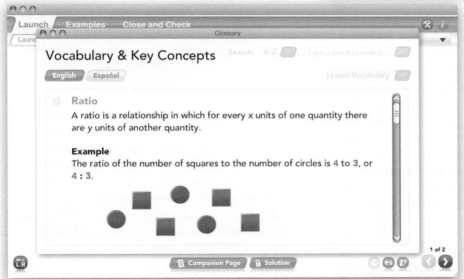

▲ The **vocabulary words** pertinent to the lesson content can be found by clicking on the 𝒱 link at the bottom of the screen. For each term, a written definition, example, audio presentation, and Spanish version of the term is provided. Teachers should check understanding of these words by having students provide their own sentence or example.

In the Teacher Resources The Lesson Preparation Notes for each lesson also include lesson objectives and key vocabulary.

1-1 Equivalent Ratios

Common Core State Standards: 7.RP.1: Compute unit rates associated with ratios of fractions, including ratios of lengths, areas and other quantities measured in like or different units.

▲ **In the Student Resources** Student Companion pages provide the **standards** that are addressed at the beginning of each lesson. Readiness Activity Sheets box the key vocabulary at the beginning of each Readiness Lesson.

PRINCIPLE 2
Frontload the Lesson

Frontloading is the use of strategies that prepare English language learners to learn new material. The goal of frontloading is to reach all ELLs by lessening the cognitive and language loads, thereby allowing them to take control of their learning process.

Frontloading involves the use of the following strategies:

Activating prior knowledge Instruction is most effective when it links knowledge and experiences students already have to new concepts. Experiences can be academic, cultural, and personal. Teachers can help students see the relationships between their prior knowledge and the new lesson through direct questioning techniques, the use of visuals and graphic organizers, and discussion. The more students know about the topic of a lesson, the more they will understand.

Building background knowledge In order to make a lesson's content accessible to ELLs, teachers may need to familiarize them with social or cultural facts and concepts of which mainstream learners are already aware. These facts and concepts may be brought out during the activating prior knowledge phase or through direct questioning and instruction.

Previewing text Previewing text serves the purpose of familiarizing students with what is to come in a lesson and putting them at ease. To preview text, teachers focus more closely on using visual supports such while walking through a lesson. In addition, English language learners should be taught discrete skills that are required for successfully reading content-area texts, such as how to read and interpret charts, tables, and graphs.

Setting a purpose for reading Teachers should help students realize that good readers focus on the message of the text. Teaching ELLs in the content areas also includes explicit instruction in the kinds of text structures they will encounter in content-area readings. In addition, it includes teaching reading strategies such as identifying the main idea and details, summarizing, and comparing and contrasting.

Making connections Teachers can extend the lesson by helping students see relationships between the lesson and other aspects of their lives. Connections can be made to other academic subjects, to current events, or to cultural traditions. By incorporating aspects of students' primary language and culture, teachers can ease the transition toward learning the content and language.

Integral to these frontloading strategies is the need for teachers to learn about the backgrounds of the English language learners. Learning about an ELL's experiences validates the student's sense of identity, increases the teacher's knowledge, and broadens the horizons of the English-speaking students in the class.

Teaching Strategies and Support for Principle 2

☐ **Prior knowledge** Determine English language learners' prior knowledge of a topic through a variety of activities. For example, have students:

- brainstorm aspects of the topic.
- construct a concept map.
- relate the topic to their personal lives through the use of examples.
- discuss a series of true-or-false statements.
- put steps of a process in a sequence chart.
- complete information in a chart.

☐ **Cultural background** Because there may be cultural or societal factors with which English language learners are unfamiliar, teachers should learn about the background of these students. Teachers can then use this knowledge to determine what additional background knowledge (facts and concepts) need to be presented. For example, before teaching a lesson using baseball statistics, teachers may need to provide some students with an explanation of the types of statistics kept in baseball, and what they mean.

☐ **Lesson feature preview** Preview the lesson by calling attention to key features: titles, visuals, captions, charts, bold or italicized words, and any special features.

☐ **Self-questioning strategies** When previewing the lesson, students should be taught to ask themselves questions such as:

- What do I think this lesson is about?
- What do I already know about this topic?
- What do the features tell me?

☐ **Predicting strategies** Have students use predicting strategies. They can predict what a word problem is going to be about by looking at its title and features. Students should always confirm any predictions after reading.

☐ **Note-taking organizers** Present a graphic organizer that students can use for taking notes. Show students how to use headings and subheadings to create an outline framework.

☐ **Set a purpose for reading** Have students set a purpose for reading so they take active control of their learning. After previewing a passage, students should ask themselves questions such as:

- What is this passage about?
- What is my purpose for reading the passage?
- How does this passage relate to the topic?

☐ **Make connections** At the end of a lesson, have students make a connection between what they have learned and with an aspect of their academic lives, or their personal lives. This activity can be done as a Think-Pair-Share exercise or in small groups.

Applying Principle 2 in *digits*

In the Lessons Opportunities for frontloading the lesson are built right into *digits* introductory presentations. The Launch or Intro features visuals, animations, and audio intended to spark students' interest in the lesson content. A host helps build background and presents the Focus Question, which can be used to informally determine what students know and whether they are ready to move on to new concepts. Themes are designed to connect to students' interests and life experience. Use the visuals, audio, and content to engage students in an introductory discussion. Guide them to talk about what they already know and to think about what they might learn.

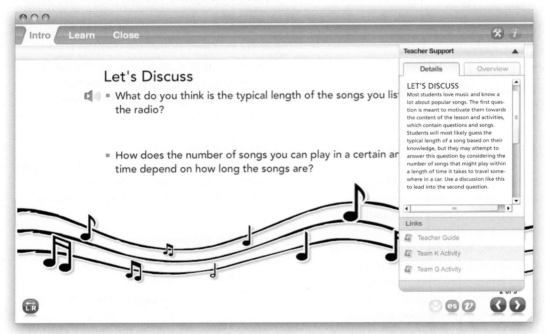

The **Teacher Support** that accompanies the lesson Intro provides an explanation of how the presentation connects to student prior knowledge. ▲

In the Teacher Resources Support for the **Topic Essential Question** and the Lesson Focus Question is found in the Lesson Plan of the Teacher Resources. It invites students to share prior experiences. It also provides a summary of the skills needed to successfully proceed with the lesson. ▼

Overview/Materials

Essential Question for Topic
Comparisons are helpful for making plans, predictions, and decisions. What math models can you use for making comparisons? Which models are helpful in which situations?

Author Intent
Many comparisons involve differences and ratios. Students with a solid grounding on the skills of dividing whole numbers, representing fractions, and simplifying fractions will have more success when they go to apply these skills to work with ratios.

Students need to master the skill of dividing by whole numbers before they can attempt to make equivalent ratios by scaling down. The skills of representing and simplifying fractions become important in the lesson "Ratios as Fractions."

This lesson prepares students for the standard listed below.

PRINCIPLE 3
Provide Comprehensible Input

Providing comprehensible input refers to making written and oral content accessible to English language learners, especially through the use of nonlinguistic supports.

Because English language learners are frequently overwhelmed by extraneous information and large blocks of text, they need help focusing on the most important concepts. With comprehensible input strategies, teachers make information and tasks clear by using step-by-step instructions, by making modifications to their speech, and by clearly defining objectives and expectations of the students.

Nonlinguistic supports teachers can use to accompany student reading include:

- photographs
- illustrations
- models
- cartoons
- graphs, charts, tables
- graphic organizers

Graphic organizers provide essential visual aids by showing at a glance the hierarchy and relationship of concepts.

Nonlinguistic supports teachers can use during class presentations include:

- gestures
- facial expressions
- props
- tone of voice
- realia (real-life visuals and objects)
- models
- demonstrations

Another effective form of comprehensible input is the "think-aloud," especially as modeled by the teacher. In a think-aloud, the teacher stops periodically and shares how to work out a problem by talking about his/her thought processes. The think-aloud shows how thinkers comprehend texts or solve difficult problems. ELLs can practice think-alouds, thereby learning to reflect and comprehend. Teachers can use the student's think-aloud to assess strengths and challenges.

A variety of comprehensible input techniques should be incorporated into lesson plans for English language learners as well as multiple exposures to new terms and concepts. Hands-on activities are particularly helpful to ELLs. The use of multimedia and other technologies will also enhance instruction.

Teaching Strategies and Support for Principle 3

☐ **Visuals** Provide meaningful visuals for English language learners. These may include pictures, images, diagrams, graphs, standard graphic organizers (e.g., Venn diagrams, charts, and concept maps), and outlines (filled-in or cloze).

☐ **Multimedia** Use a variety of media to reduce the reliance on language and place the information in a context that is more comprehensible.

- Bring realia (real-life objects) into the lessons. Have visual displays (graphs, charts, photos), objects, visitors, and authentic materials (newspaper and magazine clippings, etc.).
- Use video, audio, and CD/online interactive activities.

☐ **The five senses** Use teaching techniques that involve the other senses. For example:

- When teaching about ratios, have students taste salt water mixtures with varying ratios of salt to water.
- When teaching perimeter, have students trace the outlines of the objects being measured.

☐ **Hands-on learning** Provide hands-on experiences when appropriate to help students contextualize or personalize abstract concepts.

☐ **Demonstrations** Provide demonstrations of how something works, whether it is concrete (such as locating a point on a coordinate grid) or conceptual (absolute value).

☐ **Role-playing** Concepts can also be presented through role-playing or debates.

☐ **Think-alouds** Use think-alouds to model the kinds of question-asking strategies that students should use to construct meaning from mathematical problems. Remind students to use these questions and identify key mathematical vocabulary.

☐ **Delivery of instruction** Providing comprehensible input also refers to the delivery of instruction. For example:

- Face students when speaking.
- Speak clearly and slowly.
- Pause frequently.
- Use gestures, tone of voice, facial expressions, and emphasis as appropriate.
- Avoid the use of idioms and slang.
- Say and write instructions.

Applying Principle 3 in *digits*

In the Lessons Every lesson includes engaging animation, audio, numerous images, **charts, and tables** that will help English language learners acquire knowledge and skills. All visuals are accompanied by text and audio questions and explanations to ensure that students understand the concepts.

In the Teacher Resources Teacher Support in the lesson presentations includes a **Details column** with questions to help guide students to understanding. Note also the array of other material always accessible through icons to support students as needed. ▼

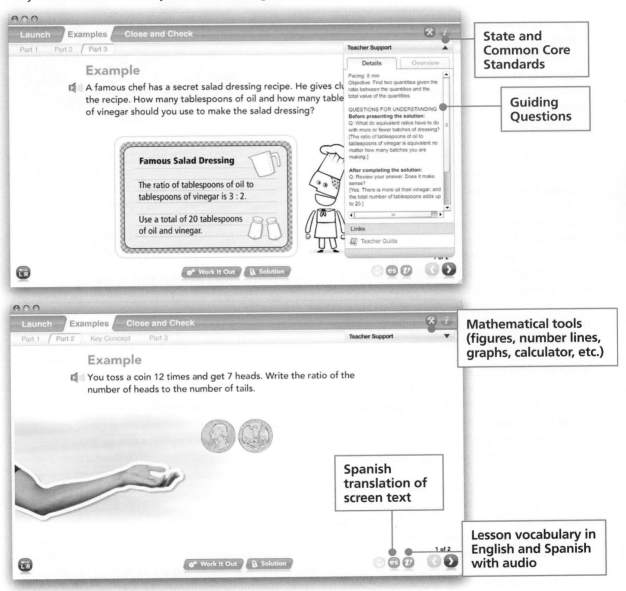

State and Common Core Standards

Guiding Questions

Mathematical tools (figures, number lines, graphs, calculator, etc.)

Spanish translation of screen text

Lesson vocabulary in English and Spanish with audio

In the Student Resources Companion Pages, Readiness Activity Sheets, and the Intervention Journal all provide visuals and text that further support the lesson presentations. These resources step students through mathematical processes and provide graphic organizers and questions that help further understanding of key concepts.

PRINCIPLE 4
Enable Language Production

Enabling language production for English language learners encompasses the four skills of listening, speaking, reading, and writing.

Because the language used by teachers and in content-area textbooks and assessment is sufficiently different from everyday spoken language, English language learners find themselves at a disadvantage in the classroom. Acquiring academic language in all four skill areas is challenging and requires at least five years of exposure to academic English to catch up with native-speaker norms. Therefore, particular attention should be paid to expanding ELLs' academic language so that they can access the learning materials and achieve success.

Brain research has ascertained that people under stress have difficulty learning and retaining new concepts. Students with limited language are naturally highly stressed. By promoting interaction among students where all contribute to a group effort, practice language, and develop relationships with one another, anxieties are reduced, thereby enabling more effective learning.

While the four language skills are intertwined, English language learners will likely not be at the same proficiency level in all four skills. Teachers will need to modify their instruction in response to students' strengths and needs in each area, keeping in mind the following concepts:

- When providing listening input to ELLs, the language must be understandable and should contain grammatical structures and vocabulary that are just beyond the current level of English language development.

- Teachers should provide appropriate "wait time" for students to respond to questions. ELLs need time to process the question and formulate an answer.

- For cultural reasons and/or due to lack of oral language skills, ELLs may not express themselves openly or may consider it disrespectful to disagree with authority figures.

- Teachers should encourage students to verbalize their understanding of the content.

- Think-alouds increase oral language production.

- In addition to frontloading and comprehensible input from the teacher, ELLs need to practice effective reading strategies, such as asking questions, predicting, and summarizing.

- There is a direct correlation between speaking and writing; by increasing oral language production, writing skills can be increased. For example, teachers can have ELLs say and write vocabulary to connect oral and written language.

- Opportunities for students to write in English in a variety of writing activities should be built into the lessons. For example, reading-response logs and journaling are activities that increase written language production.

Teaching Strategies and Support for Principle 4

☐ **Listening skills** Use audio recordings and read material aloud to develop English language learners' listening skills as well as fluency and accuracy.

☐ **Idioms, colloquialisms, and slang** Give explanations of any idioms, colloquialisms, or slang that arise.

☐ **Oral communication activities** Present specific oral communication activities. For example:

- telling or retelling stories
- role-playing
- giving instructions
- presenting a think-aloud
- explaining a process
- brainstorming
- critiquing a solution

☐ **Speaking skills** Model summarizing information and reporting. Then have students summarize and report.

☐ **Reading comprehension skills** Provide explicit teaching of reading comprehension skills. For example, teach or review summarizing, sequencing, inferring, comparing and contrasting, asking questions, drawing conclusions, distinguishing between fact and opinion, or finding main idea and details.

☐ **Reading strategies practice** Have students practice using reading strategies. For example, ask them to:

- develop their own questions.
- write the facts and information in problems.
- identify key mathematics vocabulary.

☐ **Paraphrase** Provide ELL-appropriate paraphrases of text questions.

☐ **Writing skills** Have students practice writing skills.

- review or teach the steps of the writing process.
- have students create dialogue journals for sharing problem-solving processes.

☐ **Note-taking support** Provide note-taking supports, such as writing templates, fill-in-the-blank guides, or other graphic organizers.

☐ **Self-monitoring** Provide students with checklists for monitoring their own writing, such as checklists for revising, editing, and peer editing.

☐ **Peer review** Pair ELLs with partners for peer feedback on their problem-solving processes.

☐ **Scoring rubrics** Provide scoring rubrics for oral and written assignments and assessments. For example, students' writing can be evaluated for focus, ideas, order, writer's voice, word choice, and sentence structure. Students should be evaluated according to their proficiency levels.

Applying Principle 4 in *digits*

In the Lessons Enabling language production consists of students practicing their listening, speaking, reading, and writing skills. To develop English language learners' listening and speaking skills, use any lesson presentation. Have ELLs listen to the **audio presentation** as they read the text presented and then have them use the language of the presentation as they solve the problem. ▼

Audio ◄‹)) A gift shop sells boxes of fruit online, including this box of apples and pears. Use numbers to compare the fruit in three different ways.

Reflect Choose one of your comparisons. Describe a situation where you could use it.

_____

_____

▲ **In the Student Resources** Each Launch activity includes opportunities for students to write (in their Companions) and report about their solutions.

4. Error Analysis A student looks at the graph below and says that the rate of change is $\frac{2}{1}$ and the initial value is 2. Explain why this is incorrect.

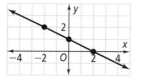

◄ **Companion** pages also include writing opportunities to explain mathematical terms and to analyze work. Students are asked to answer questions, explain their processes, and show understanding of key vocabulary.

In the Teacher Resource Prompts found in the Teacher Support menu provide students with the opportunity to present their work and thereby practice their speaking skills. ▼

🎬 **Connect Your Learning** Move to the Connect Your Learning screen. Use the Launch to talk about strategy. Some students may have written the equations first and then drawn the lines, while others did the reverse. Have students talk about the advantages and disadvantages of each approach. Students may benefit from hearing other opinions about how to approach a problem like this.

PRINCIPLE 5
Assess for Content and Language Understanding

An ever-increasing emphasis on assessment requires that all students—including English language learners—achieve the same high standards. Yet below-level language proficiency can have a negative impact on an ELL's success in the content areas. It is, therefore, essential to use assessment results as a way to identify an ELL's strengths and challenges.

Three types of assessments are key to instruction for all students, including ELLs: diagnostic assessment, formative assessment, and summative assessment.

Diagnostic assessment Diagnostic assessment is used for placing English language learners into the appropriate class, as well as for providing a diagnosis of strengths and challenges.

Formative assessment Formative assessment is part of the instructional process. It includes ongoing informal and formal assessment, reviews, and classroom observations. Informal assessments include class discussions, teacher observations, self- and peer-assessment, and teacher-student conversations. Formal assessments include quizzes, tests, and presentations.

Formative assessment is used to improve the teaching and learning process—which is particularly important in regards to English language learners. By using formative assessments, teachers can target an ELL's specific problem areas, adapt instruction, and intervene earlier rather than later.

Summative assessment Summative assessment occurs at the end of a specific period and evaluates student competency and the effectiveness of instruction. Examples are mid-year and final exams, state tests, and national tests.

Federal and state law requires that all students, including English language learners, be assessed in reading, math, and science.

Assessment accommodations Assessment accommodations for ELLs can minimize the negative impact of the lack of language proficiency when assessing in the content areas. These accommodations can be used for formal and informal assessments.

Possible assessment accommodations include: time extensions, use of bilingual dictionaries and glossaries, repeated readings of problems, use of dual-language assessments, allowing written responses in the native language, and separate testing locations.

Teaching Strategies and Support for Principle 5

☐ **Informal assessment** Use a variety of informal assessments for ELLs including retelling, demonstrating, and illustrating.

☐ **Content area log** Have students keep a "content area log." Use a two-column format with the headings What I Understand and What I Don't Understand. Follow up with students on the What I Don't Understand items so that they can move those items into the other column.

☐ **Portfolios** Portfolios are a practical way to assess student progress. Provide specific examples of what to include in a portfolio, including examples of speaking and writing. Some portfolio items might be:

- written assignments
- recordings of speaking samples, oral presentations, or think-alouds
- exercise sheets
- scoring rubrics and written evaluations by the teacher
- tests and quizzes

☐ **Formal assessments** Use a variety of formal assessments such as practice tests, real tests, and oral and written assessments.

☐ **Assessment format** Create tests with a variety of assessment formats, including dictation, multiple choice, cloze, and open-response formats.

☐ **Standardized tests** Have students practice taking standardized tests by using released test items. These are often available online from your state department of education or district website.

☐ **Academic vocabulary** Explicitly teach the academic English words, phrases, and constructions that often appear in standardized test items. This might include *best*, *both*, *except*, and *probably*.

☐ **Restate directions** When giving directions, restate the directions in simplified English, repeat the directions, and emphasize key words.

☐ **Repeat directions** Verify a student's understanding of the directions by having the student repeat the directions in his/her own words.

☐ **Bilingual glossaries** Provide students with bilingual glossaries of academic vocabulary.

☐ **Written assessments** Writing portions of assessments are generally the most difficult for English language learners. Therefore, the writing process should be practiced. Teachers should carefully guide students through the prewriting step with examples of brainstorming, outlining, using a graphic organizer, etc.

Applying Principle 5 in *digits*

In the Lessons Diagnostic and formative assessment are provided in the lesson presentations. Teachers can use the Readiness Lesson as an informal diagnostic assessment to determine if students have sufficient mastery of foundational concepts to proceed with new material. Within all On-level Lessons, each Example ends with a **Got It?** problem that serves as a formative assessment of understanding. For Intervention Lessons, the Journal pages provide formative assessment. ▼

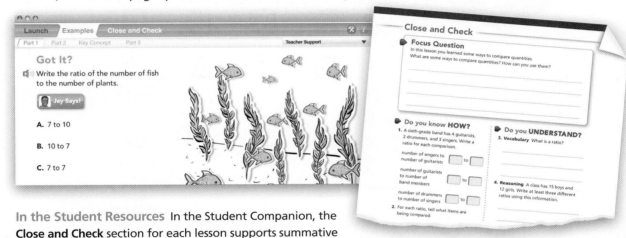

In the Student Resources In the Student Companion, the **Close and Check** section for each lesson supports summative assessment of understanding for the lesson. Writing activities give students the opportunity to demonstrate understanding of key vocabulary. ▲

In the Teacher Resources Formal testing can be done electronically or on paper through exams generated by Math XL. Tests may be generated randomly or teachers can pick the specific problems to generate a customized test. When tests are taken electronically there is an automatic scoring feature.

In Homework The online option for homework provides students with **immediate feedback** on their work. When students provide a correct answer, they receive a message telling them so. When they are incorrect, they get a hint about what they may be doing wrong. ▶

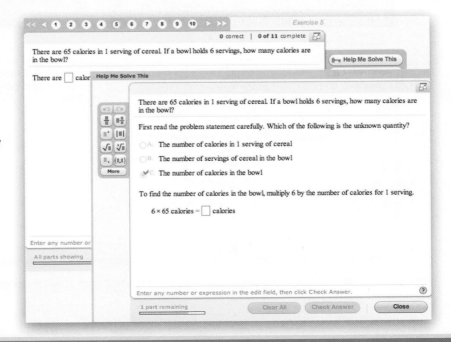

Appendix A

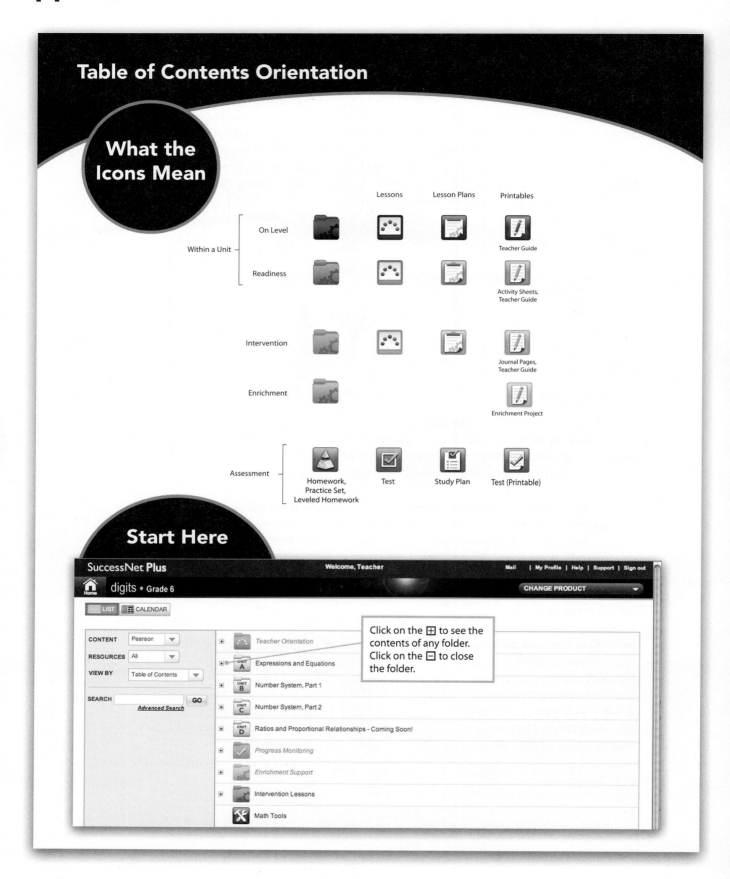

Table of Contents Orientation

What the Icons Mean

		Lessons	Lesson Plans	Printables
Within a Unit	On Level			Teacher Guide
	Readiness			Activity Sheets, Teacher Guide
	Intervention			Journal Pages, Teacher Guide
	Enrichment			Enrichment Project

Assessment				
Homework, Practice Set, Leveled Homework	Test	Study Plan	Test (Printable)

Start Here

SuccessNet **Plus**   Welcome, Teacher   Mail | My Profile | Help | Support | Sign out

Home digits • Grade 6   CHANGE PRODUCT ▼

LIST   CALENDAR

CONTENT Pearson ▼
RESOURCES All ▼
VIEW BY Table of Contents ▼
SEARCH [____] GO
Advanced Search

- Teacher Orientation
- UNIT A Expressions and Equations
- UNIT B Number System, Part 1
- UNIT C Number System, Part 2
- UNIT D Ratios and Proportional Relationships - Coming Soon!
- Progress Monitoring
- Enrichment Support
- Intervention Lessons
- Math Tools

> Click on the ⊞ to see the contents of any folder. Click on the ⊟ to close the folder.

Table of Contents Orientation

SuccessNet Plus

Welcome, Teacher   Mail | My Profile | Help | Support | Sign out

digits • Grade 6   CHANGE PRODUCT ▼

LIST   CALENDAR

CONTENT [Pearson ▼]
RESOURCES [All ▼]
VIEW BY [Table of Contents ▼]

SEARCH [_____] GO
Advanced Search

Inside Each Unit

- ⊞ *Teacher Orientation*
- ⊞ UNIT A Expressions and Equations
- ⊞ UNIT B Number System, Part 1
- ⊞ UNIT C Number System, Part 2
- ⊟ UNIT D Ratios and Proportional Relationships - Coming Soon!
  - *Unit D Readiness Assessment*
  - ⊞ *Unit D Enrichment Support*
  - ⊟ TOPIC 10 Ratios
    - ⊞ *Readiness Lesson r10: Working with Playlists*
    - Lesson 10-1: Ratios
    - ⊞ *10-1 Homework*
    - *10-1 Teacher Guide* 🔒
    - 10-1: Ratios 🔒
    - Lesson 10-2: Exploring Equivalent Ratios
    - ⊞ *10-2 Homework*
    - *10-2 Teacher Guide* 🔒
    - 10-2: Exploring Equivalent Ratios 🔒
    - Lesson 10-3: Equivalent Ratios
    - ⊞ *10-3 Homework*
    - *10-3 Teacher Guide* 🔒
    - 10-3: Equivalent Ratios 🔒
    - Lesson 10-4: Ratios as Fractions
    - ⊞ *10-4 Homework*

Options
- Customize Content
- Preview
- View Content
- Assign
- Get Information

Unit Folders contain On-Level and Readiness folders and files.

Topic Folders Inside each Topic folder you will find icons that indicate
- on-level lessons
- teaching resources

Homework Open Homework folders to access MathXL homework files.

Launch an Item To launch content, click on the item's name. You can also click on the dropdown button, and then choose Preview from the Options dropdown. For leveled homework, choose between Level G or Level K.

Items that are italicized are hidden from students in their Practice view. However, they are assignable to students.

🔒 This icon indicates the file is for teachers only and therefore is unassignable to students.

Appendix A *continued*

Table of Contents Orientation

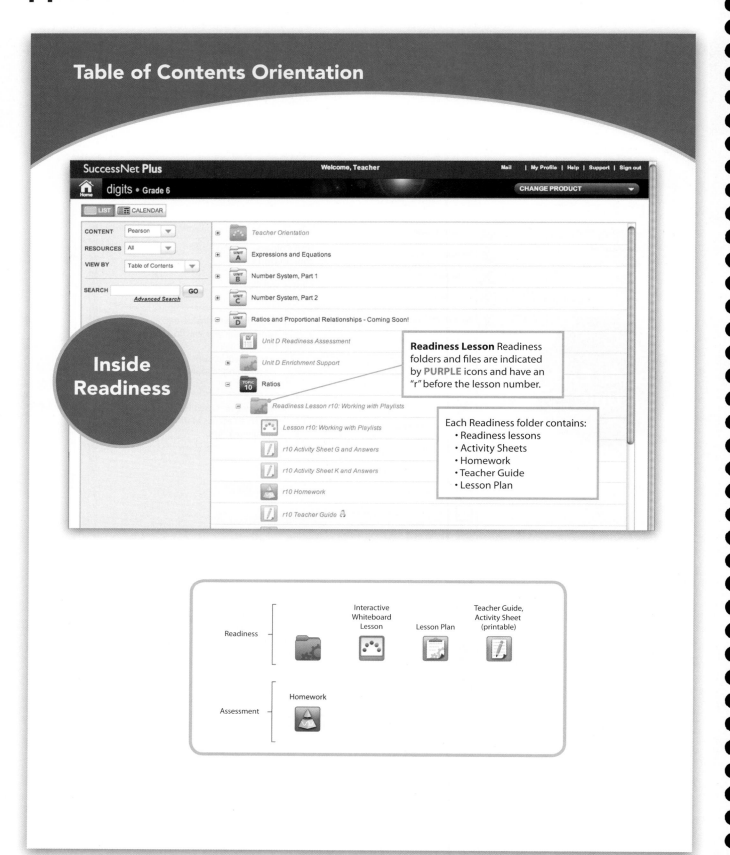

SuccessNet **Plus**   Welcome, Teacher   Mail | My Profile | Help | Support | Sign out

digits • Grade 6   CHANGE PRODUCT

LIST | CALENDAR

CONTENT Pearson
RESOURCES All
VIEW BY Table of Contents

SEARCH GO
Advanced Search

Inside Readiness

- Teacher Orientation
- UNIT A Expressions and Equations
- UNIT B Number System, Part 1
- UNIT C Number System, Part 2
- UNIT D Ratios and Proportional Relationships - Coming Soon!
  - Unit D Readiness Assessment
  - Unit D Enrichment Support
  - TOPIC 10 Ratios
    - Readiness Lesson r10: Working with Playlists
      - Lesson r10: Working with Playlists
      - r10 Activity Sheet G and Answers
      - r10 Activity Sheet K and Answers
      - r10 Homework
      - r10 Teacher Guide

Readiness Lesson Readiness folders and files are indicated by **PURPLE** icons and have an "r" before the lesson number.

Each Readiness folder contains:
- Readiness lessons
- Activity Sheets
- Homework
- Teacher Guide
- Lesson Plan

Readiness —
Interactive Whiteboard Lesson | Lesson Plan | Teacher Guide, Activity Sheet (printable)

Assessment —
Homework

Table of Contents Orientation

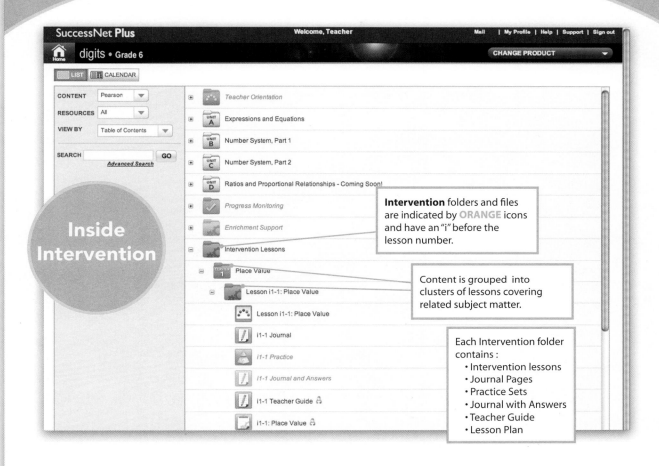

Inside Intervention

Intervention folders and files are indicated by ORANGE icons and have an "i" before the lesson number.

Content is grouped into clusters of lessons covering related subject matter.

Each Intervention folder contains :
- Intervention lessons
- Journal Pages
- Practice Sets
- Journal with Answers
- Teacher Guide
- Lesson Plan

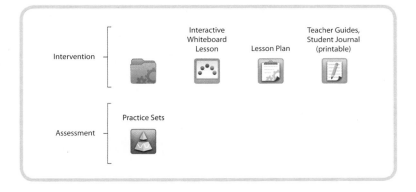